# HORSE CARE TIPS

*from*

*to*

Quick and easy ways
to take better care of your horse.

From the editors of EQUUS magazine

## Horse Care Tips from A to Z
*edited by Mary Kay Kinnish*

©2000 PRIMEDIA Enthusiast Publications, Inc.
d/b/a/ PRIMEDIA Equine Group

PRIMEDIA Equine Group
656 Quince Orchard Road, #600
Gaithersburg, MD 20878

Library of Congress Catalog Card Number: 00-103350
ISBN: 1-929164-03-3

Book and cover design by Sharon Reuter, Reuter & Associates
Cover photographs of horse, apple and carrot by Christel Sexton

# Table of Contents

## Six strategies for aging gracefully

A number of factors influence how a horse will age. Conscientious care that steers clear of extremes will preserve his well-being and prolong his useful life. Here are six strategies that will help your horse to feel young:

1. *Keep him on a sound feeding program.* Overfeeding can take its toll as a horse gets older, precipitating digestive upsets, skeletal weakness and possibly cardiovascular failure.

2. *Maintain regular vaccination and deworming schedules.* Infections and infestations have a cumulative effect over the course of a horse's lifetime.

3. *Increase the intensity of training gradually.* Stress on young joints may precipitate arthritis and other forms of lameness in the equine senior citizen.

4. *Keep him fit.* Getting a horse in condition after a long layoff becomes more difficult with each passing year. Similarly, strenuous weekend workouts following five days of inactivity predispose a horse to injury.

5. *Rehabilitate injuries as they occur.* Prompt treatment—especially when a horse is young—takes advantage of the body's natural healing mechanisms and helps prevent lameness later in life.

6. *Adapt athletic demands.* Rather than continue to push a horse who's no longer at the top of his game, introduce him to an activity that makes the most of his strength, endurance and temperament.

## Anhidrosis: Suddenly your hot horse can't sweat

Anhidrosis—a complete lack of sweating in an overheated horse—is a **Red Alert** situation, requiring a veterinarian's immediate attention. A failure of the endocrine system's temperature-regulating mechanism, anhidrosis can occur suddenly and unexpectedly. The resulting buildup of internal heat is life-threatening: Immediately move the afflicted horse into the shade, cool him with a bath of water and rubbing alcohol, and call your veterinarian. Although the condition is not reversible, anhidrotic horses can be maintained in air-conditioned quarters during hot weather and ridden in cold to moderate temperatures the rest of the year, with appropriate cooling measures taken during exercise.

**TERMINOLOGY**

AEROBIC EXERCISE

*The activity level that utilizes a horse's capacity to supply oxygen to the cells. Occurs during work at relatively slow, steady rates and develops a horse's endurance.*

## How to recognize an equine allergy

Allergy is an overreaction of your horse's immune system to invading foreign particles. A complex internal response, it's not entirely understood. Research has yet to reveal why a particular horse's immune system reacts to some invaders with normal, self-protective mechanisms but overreacts to others in self-destructive ways. Neither is it clear why a given substance may trigger an allergic response in one horse but be well tolerated by others in the same environment.

Most battles between allergens and the body's immune system take place in the skin, the respiratory system and, occasionally, the digestive tract. They can be relatively mild and pass in a short time (an acute reaction) or they may grow more severe and persistent (a chronic reaction). You may suspect that your horse has an allergy if he exhibits any of the following signs:

- head tossing
- sneezing or snorting as if he's trying to clear his nostrils
- coughing—particularly if the cough is dry and unproductive
- nasal congestion
- runny eyes
- repeated foot stomping
- rubbing the nose and eyes on a front leg, fence post or wall
- labored breathing
- hives (raised, painless bumps on the skin, which may be localized or appear all over the body)
- excessive itchiness
- sudden, brief and explosive cramping diarrhea
- exercise intolerance.

Changes in management may be enough to eliminate an allergen from your horse's environment, or medical intervention may be necessary to resolve the problem completely. Your veterinarian can help to identify the source of your horse's allergy and recommend the appropriate course of treatment.

## Handling an abscess in a hoof

Few conditions are as swiftly and completely disabling as an abscess in a horse's hoof. Most abscesses appear very rapidly following an injury of major or minor proportion that allows bacteria to enter the hoof. The resultant infection inside the hoof is excruciatingly painful for the horse because there is little room for a pus pocket to expand. The location of the abscess—either under the wall or under the sole—determines where it will rupture if it's left untreated. Wall abscesses usually expand upward toward the coronary band. Pus under the sole, bars or frog usually works its way toward the heel.

A hoof abscess will cause a horse to be three-legged lame. He'll be extremely sensitive to having his foot probed with thumb pressure or a hoof tester. You may notice that the pulse in the main artery of his affected leg is throbbing—beating harder, not faster—and the veins over his ankle and alongside his tendons will bulge. Inspection of the hoof may reveal a small hole in the sole or frog, or a black spot in the white-line area. In some cases, a soft, pale pimple of discoloration may appear at the coronary band, or you may find a red mark on the horny sole.

Treatment involves

1. Draining the abscess (call your veterinarian or farrier to establish an adequate drainage channel).
2. Soaking the hoof in warm water and Epsom salts to promote drainage.
3. Flushing the hole with a germicide or oxidizing agent, such as hydrogen peroxide, to kill any remaining bacteria and dry the wound.
4. Packing the hoof with a poultice or drawing salve, such as ichthammol, to further encourage drainage.
5. Bandaging or otherwise protecting the drainage hole and the bottom of the hoof.

Though you may be tempted to reach for an antibiotic when your horse has a hoof abscess, keep in mind that the location of the pus pocket—between the tissue and the hoof—is beyond the reach of any such medication given by mouth or injection.

Once treatment is initiated, recovery will take about a week.

## Antibiotics: Here's how they work

Antimicrobial drugs either kill or suppress infectious organisms, allowing an ailing horse to mobilize his own defenses and return the infected tissues or organ to normal operations. Different organisms may be susceptible to different drugs.

*Bactericidal drugs* are "germ" killers that act in the following ways:

- The penicillin group family blocks the enzyme necessary for bacteria to maintain resilient cell walls, causing the microbes to explode.
- The aminoglycocide antibiotics gentimicin and neomycin alter a life-sustaining protein-production mechanism within vulnerable bacteria.
- Sulfa drugs kill many kinds of bacteria by disrupting essential folic-acid metabolism.

**Bacteriostatic drugs** hold the line on reproduction so bacterial populations won't overrun the host's system:

- Tetracycline and erythromycin enter susceptible microbes and disrupt protein production necessary in their reproduction.
- Rifampin enters bacterial nuclei to alter cell metabolism and disable the genetic material that directs reproduction.

## Protect against the onset of arthritis

You know how important oil is to a car's engine. Without it, parts rub against each other, creating friction, heat, wear and possibly catastrophic breakdown.

The joints of your horse's body have a similar need for lubrication. Although the cartilage covering the ends of the bones helps to absorb concussion, synovial fluid—a sticky, transparent substance secreted by the synovial membrane—is crucial to joint function. Like the motor oil in your car's engine, synovial fluid keeps the parts in your horse's joints separated and gliding over each other smoothly.

When a horse develops arthritis, this system breaks down. Trauma, infection, poor conformation, age or abnormal stress triggers inflammation within a joint, which, in turn, causes the synovial fluid to degrade. Without sufficient lubrication, the cartilage gradually erodes, eventually thickening and inflaming the joint capsule. In response, the body attempts to strengthen the joint by producing excess bone. The bone spurs that eventually develop are painful and limit joint movement.

To reduce the likelihood of your horse developing arthritis, adapt his athletic use to his conformation, shoe him properly, exercise him regularly and take care not to overwork him. If he does become lame, consult your veterinarian. He'll determine whether the problem is arthritis and offer a plan of action based on the location and extent of the condition.

## When is it best to bandage?

Bandaging wounds has its pros and cons. In deciding whether to bandage a wound that your horse has suffered, location and depth are key considerations:

- *Leave high wounds uncovered.* Put low wounds under wraps. Uncontaminated wounds above the elbow and stifle are likely to scab over and heal well on their own. This rapid response is a function of the relative immobility of the horse's torso and the superior circulation at or above heart level. In contrast, lower-leg wounds often are irritated by dirt, motion and abrasion. The high capillary pressure in the legs—resulting from their location below the heart—promotes the formation of proud flesh, an excessive growth of granulation tissue that won't heal. Carefully applied bandages often are beneficial for wounds at or below the knees and hocks.

- *Leave shallow wounds unbandaged.* Keep "full-thickness" wounds covered. Once they're thoroughly cleaned, superficial scrapes and abrasions are best left open to the air, because they form strong scabs almost immediately. A full-thickness wound—one that penetrates all skin layers so that the edges separate or can be pulled apart to reveal underlying structures—does not form a strong scab and can invite deep infection if left exposed. For wounds that require stitching, ask the attending veterinarian about bandaging recommendations.

In general, simple wounds above the knee and hock do just fine without bandages, while most full-thickness wounds heal better with bandages. New skin formed under bandages is fragile and may require surface ointments or a loose covering until it toughens up enough to face the elements.

## To stop a wound from bleeding…

Immediately apply pressure directly to the wound. Use clean gauze or woven cloth, and after a few minutes, check to see if your efforts have slowed the flow. Profuse bleeding or blood that spurts out bright red with a pulsating action likely is coming from an artery that's been damaged. Use a thick fabric pad to apply heavy pressure to the wound for at least 30 minutes or until the veterinarian arrives. A pressure bandage—made by placing gauze or another absorbent material over the wound and then wrapping it with an elastic bandage—also can help to control bleeding from an artery.

If, instead, you see dark-colored blood leaking or flowing from the wound, a vein has been damaged. In this case, cover the area with gauze and apply pressure for five to 10 minutes, then remove the fabric. If bleeding resumes, repeat the procedure, maintaining pressure on the wound for another five to 10 minutes, or until the hemorrhaging stops.

As you minister to your horse's wound, do what you can to keep him calm. Agitation or tension can boost heart rate and blood pressure, increasing bleeding and progressively weakening your horse, putting him at risk of shock and possibly death.

**TERMINOLOGY**

**BRACHIOCEPHALICUS**

*The longest muscle in the horse's body, running from the forearm over the shoulder, then along the side of the neck up to the head. Assists in pulling the head to the side.*

## It's bath time

To get your horse spick-and-span without a speck of trouble, first gather the tools and supplies you'll need to give him a bath: a bucket or two, shampoos, conditioner, sponges, towels and a sweat scraper. Then find a place that's relatively level and won't become a mud hole while you're working.

If your horse will stand quietly on cross-ties, or better still, cooperate while ground tied, you can probably get the job done on your own. But if your horse objects to being bathed, or is getting his first bath, ask a helper to hold him.

Start by hosing your horse's legs. Work your way from bottom to top, from the underside of his neck to his belly and in between his legs. Then move on to the top of his neck, over his back and hindquarters.

After thoroughly dousing your horse with water, begin sudsing with a mild shampoo. Take care not to let the soap dry before rinsing and make sure your efforts are thorough. Soapy residue can irritate your horse's skin far more than it bothers your own.

To clean your horse's mane and tail, gently massage the shampoo deep into the roots of the hair, especially at the crest of the neck and the underside of the tail. If your horse will stand for it, dip his entire tail in a bucket of sudsy water and swish it around. After rinsing, you can control tangles by applying a conditioner before combing.

Be extra cautious when you wash your horse's face and head so you don't get soap and water in his eyes or ears. It's also best to use a clean sponge for the final rinse of his more sensitive areas, such as his face and genitalia.

Finally, squeegee the excess water off with a sweat scraper or towel him off. Be careful to dry your horse's heels so there's no danger of them becoming chapped and developing scratches. You also might want to wait until your horse dries completely before you turn him out. Otherwise, he may be inclined to roll in mud and dirt to remove the moisture from his wet coat.

## 10 tips for battling bugs

1. Remove anything from around the barn and pasture that holds rainwater, such as old tires and unused buckets, and fill in persistent or perennial puddles.
2. Do not spread fresh, uncomposted manure on horse pastures you intend to use before the manure decomposes.
3. Don't overcrowd pastures.
4. Clean up grain spills and decaying vegetation, such as grass clippings and uneaten hay in pastures.
5. Keep water buckets clean and water fresh.
6. Deworm your horses on a regular schedule.
7. Apply insecticide and repellent frequently.
8. Outfit your horses in fly masks.
9. For pastured horses, provide a shady shelter as a refuge from biting flies.
10. Remove manure from stalls daily and from pastures twice a week, and compost or dispose of it.

## Stop your horse from bucking

For some horses, a buck is simply a by-product of exuberance. For others, it's a dangerous equine temper tantrum, and you're probably not fond of either sort. Bucking is essentially a series of acrobatic jumps in which the horse's front legs leave the ground and, before they have a chance to land again, the hind end follows. Different horses may add embellishments, such as the midair twist and the highly effective shoulder drop upon landing.

To ride out a buck to the best of your ability, try the following tactics:

- Sit well back in the saddle to avoid going off over the shoulder, and push your legs in front of you for support.
- Snatch up on the reins to bring the horse's head up. He can't

**VITAL STATISTICS**

BLOOD-CELL COUNTS

*Your horse's red blood cells (RBCs) supply oxygen to every tissue throughout his body. A measurement known as packed cell volume (PCV) indicates the percentage of RBCs in the blood. A normal PCV for a horse at rest is 35 to 40. At work, it increases to between 55 and 65. (Because your horse doesn't need as much oxygen when he's resting, nearly half of his red blood cells withdraw from circulation and are stored in his spleen until they're needed.) In contrast, your horse's white blood cells (WBCs) fight infection. Roughly 6,000 to 12,000 WBCs in a blood sample is normal.*

buck effectively with his head above chest level.
- Try to get him moving forward, instead of up and down.
- Head uphill, if there's one nearby. Hill climbing shifts the horse's balance so it's almost impossible for him to buck. Watch out for the downgrade, however.

In addition, you can use two lengths of baling twine to make a simple overcheck to prevent bucking. Tie one end of each string to the front D rings or through the gullet of your saddle. About halfway up the horse's neck, cross the two strands, looping one under the other, or, instead of the crossover, run the twine through the brow band loops. Finally, tie the free ends to the bit rings, allowing the horse enough freedom for normal head carriage but not enough that he can lower his chin below his chest. He'll get a self-correcting jolt on the bit each time he tries to get his head into bucking position.

You'll also want to rule out any physical ailments, starting with saddle fit and back soreness, that could be provoking your horse to buck. If pain does not seem to be the cause, isolate the stimulus or occasion that elicits the leaps, then focus your retraining program on changing his behavior under those circumstances.

## From baby to barn

To help save time and money:

Use *baby oil* to untangle and add shine to your horse's mane and tail. The oil also makes it easier to remove burrs. It moisturizes coronary bands and keeps chestnuts soft.

Apply *baby powder* to clean legs to whiten socks and stockings.

Use a *disposable diaper* when your horse needs a durable and waterproof hoof bandage. Just wrap the diaper around the hoof and secure it with tape. Adding duct tape along the bottom edge keeps the diaper from wearing as the horse moves around. Cloth diapers also make good wraps and padding.

Recycle *baby-food jars* into bridle hangers. Simply nail the lids to the wall and screw jars into each.

Ensure your peace of mind by putting a *baby monitor* in the barn to keep tabs on a sick horse or a pregnant mare. Hang the transmitter out of reach of the stall-bound horse, and keep the receiver with you.

## The telling signs of colic

Colic, a broad term for "pain in the belly," can indicate a variety of digestive problems, ranging from minor to life threatening. The condition's possible causes are numerous, but constipation, indigestion, parasite damage, ingestion of excessive amounts of grain and exhaustion head the list. A case of colic can quickly worsen, so it's important to recognize its signs early on.

Although the intensity of a horse's discomfort depends on the severity of the attack and his own reaction to pain, these signs suggest the onset of colic:

- restlessness and anxiety, accompanied by slight sweating
- little interest in food
- a tendency to nose or kick at the belly
- lying down for extended periods, lying down and getting up repeatedly, or attempting to roll repeatedly.

If your horse displays any of these signs, call your veterinarian at once. He'll evaluate the situation and recommend the course of action that will ease your horse's discomfort.

## Choke versus choking

Two sound-alike conditions—equine "choke" and choking—pose distinctly different threats to horses. Choke is the lesser danger because it is the esophagus—

the channel that relays chewed food from the throat to the stomach—that is blocked. In contrast, a choking horse has an obstruction in his windpipe—an extremely rare and desperate situation.

Choke can be caused by gluttonous bolting of feed, excessively dry rations, or ingestion of an unchewed object such as a chunk of carrot, apple or wood. A horse suffering from choke makes repeated gulping efforts to swallow, oozes alarming amounts of saliva mixed with food from his nose and appears somewhat distressed.

If you suspect that your horse's esophagus is blocked, tie him away from food and water, allowing him enough rope to lower his head. Then call your veterinarian. If the obstruction has not dissolved before the veterinarian arrives, he may administer small amounts of lubricants to help the mass pass to the stomach. He also may administer antibiotics to prevent infection. Choke can cause serious complications when allowed to continue for several hours, or when saliva, food or other foreign matter leaks into a horse's lungs. When treated promptly, choke usually has little lasting effect.

An airway obstruction responsible for choking usually arises from an inflammatory disease, allergic reaction, or trauma such as a kick to the throat. A choking horse makes an audible snoring sound as he strains to get air into his lungs. He may become increasingly frantic or "crazed" with the sense of suffocation or asphyxia. Call your veterinarian immediately. Minutes can make the difference in the horse's chances of survival. A swift, powerful kick in the belly, just behind the ribs, may force enough air back up the trachea to dislodge an object, but it won't have an effect in cases of disease, allergy or trauma. Usually the only real chance a choking horse has for survival is an immediate tracheotomy (cutting into the windpipe to allow air to enter below the obstruction), followed by manipulation or surgery to clear the airway.

**VITAL STATISTICS**

CAPILLARY REFILL TIME

*To help you gauge your horse's health status, check his capillary refill time. Place you thumbtip on the gum above an upper tooth or below a lower tooth, pressing hard and long enough to create a white spot on the pink surface. Release the pressure and count how many seconds pass before the blood flushes fully back into the white spot. Between one and two seconds is normal. Slower refill time may indicate low blood pressure, shock or dehydration.*

## Ways to warm up your cold-backed horse

If your otherwise healthy horse drops his back whenever he's saddled or mounted, he may be "cold-backed." So named because it resembles the reaction a person might have to a cold hand on the back, this equine response has nothing to do with temperature. Instead, a cold-backed horse is probably telling you that he is in, or anticipates, pain.

The first step in resolving the problem is to identify any possible sources of discomfort. Check the fit of your saddle and the other pieces of tack that you're using. Evaluate your horse's workload and training schedule, since many cases of equine back soreness result from a work regimen that asks for too much too soon. Also consider whether you're contributing to the problem. Ask an instructor to scrutinize your riding technique and make suggestions. Imbalance on your part or an unsteady seat may be bruising or straining your horse's back.

In many cases, a cold-backed response can be prevented with one or two simple measures. Longeing a horse for 10 to 20 minutes prior to saddling him may loosen his back muscles enough to relieve minor discomfort associated with saddling or mounting. For a horse that seems to have an innately tender back, therapeutic saddle pads, designed for extra cushioning and shock absorption, may do the trick. Acute soreness may require rest and medication to interrupt the pain cycle and start recovery.

## Aftercare to avoid castration complications

One of the most commonly performed surgeries in equine medicine, castration also is one of the most likely to lead to local infection The surgical site will be contaminated. That's because it's usually done on the farm, where bacteria are plentiful, and the wound is left open to allow inflammatory fluids to drain. If your colt undergoes this rite of passage at home, the aftercare you provide can prevent complications.

Ask your veterinarian to administer antibiotics before surgery begins, so the serum exuded will fight bacteria. Then continue the antibiotics for three to four additional days. The stretchable connective tissue around the scrotum is capable of swelling to 10 times its normal size—a common aftermath of castration. If swelling seals the wound shut, trapped bacteria can proliferate and inflammatory fluids accumulate. Hose twice daily with cold water, and massage the area gently to prevent this misery. Hosing is sufficient to keep the wound clean. Manual cleaning may disrupt healing and probably won't be tolerated by the horse. Hand-walk the patient to promote circulation, but keep it slow since vigorous movement may irritate the area.

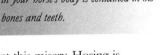

These simple measures, along with your veterinarian's specific instructions, should lead to an uneventful recovery. Stay alert for the following signs, which indicate that something is amiss and veterinary attention is warranted:
- an abnormal stance or odd hind-leg action
- swelling extending beyond the incision area to the belly or groin
- extreme tenderness around the incision
- a protrusion from the incision
- fever, depression, loss of appetite.

## Corn oil improves coat condition

Add two to four tablespoons of corn oil to a horse's daily ration to help make his coat gleam. Giving him more than that will provide a significant energy (calorie) bonus, which will be transformed into extra energy and/or additional body fat. Up to two cups of corn oil added to the daily ration is beneficial for horses who are

- in strenuous work
- recovering from illness
- too thin
- having trouble staying warm.

Keep in mind, however, that a horse's gut can absorb no more than two cups of corn oil a day. If he is given more than that, his stool will become abnormally soft, leaving you with additional stall-cleaning and grooming chores.

Another option to explore when you're looking to improve your horse's condition is the variety of specialized supplements formulated to address horse's specific health-care needs. Consult with your veterinarian for a recommendation and visit your local feed store to select the product that will provide the right mix of nutrients for your horse.

## Cold-weather questions & answers

Just because the mercury plunges below freezing doesn't mean you must put your riding schedule on hold. Yet the following cold-weather questions call for commonsense compromises between your needs and your horse's:

**Question 1:** To clip or not to clip?

If you ride regularly throughout the winter, you may decide that the extra demands of caring for a clipped horse are offset by the convenience of not having to deal with sweat-drenched winter fur after you ride. The style of clip will be dictated by the vigor of your horse's workouts and the conditions in which you live. The trace clip removes hair from along the lower part of the neck, sides and belly, to speed cooling while sparing most of the horse's natural protection. The blanket clip involves shearing all the hair from the extremities while leaving the upper torso covered. The hunter clip skips the legs and (optionally) the saddle area and shaves the rest. The full-body clip takes it all off.

**Question 2:** Are blankets in order?

You'll need to blanket the more completely clipped horse and any of the finer-skinned creatures who regularly shiver in their stalls and paddocks. But resist the urge to swaddle your horse in layers and layers of clothing. Overheating is not only uncomfortable, it can be unhealthy, contributing to skin disorders and, through chilling brought on by trapped sweat, lowered resistance to respiratory diseases.

**Question 3:** Are there special cooling-out considerations?

After work, your horse's body needs adequate time to dissipate the cellular waste products of exercise, but it's very important that he doesn't become chilled. A gradual decrease in his working pace during the last mile or two of your ride will ensure that he arrives back at the barn sufficiently cool. Once you dismount, hand-walk your horse in a sheltered area. To prevent a rapid loss of body heat, cover his back and hindquarters with a stable sheet until his breathing returns to normal and his sweaty coat begins to dry. Monitor his breathing and his pulse rate, and keep him walking until they return to walking levels of eight to 20 breaths and 40 to 50 beats per minute.

## Drugs 101

Since you're the one left holding the medicine bag after the veterinarian leaves, you need a working knowledge of drug categories and actions if you are to manage your horses' treatments safely and effectively.

- Analgesics, such as Banamine, control pain associated with colic and traumatic injuries.
- Anthelmintics, commonly called dewormers, kill internal parasites.
- Antibiotics fight infection by killing bacteria. The two most commonly prescribed for horses are penicillin and gentamicin.
- Nonsteroidal anti-inflammatory drugs (NSAIDs) control inflammation from injuries. Phenylbutazone ("bute") is the most common in equine use.
- Most NSAIDs are also antipyretics, drugs that reduce fever, making them useful in treating feverish illnesses, such as the flu.
- Bronchodilators relax and open airways inside the lungs, providing relief to horses with respiratory allergies, often called heaves.
- Corticosteroids are heavy-duty inflammation reducers used to control intense swelling associated with such conditions as allergic reactions and uveitis, a severe inflammation of the eye.
- Sedatives (Rompun, Dormosedan) depress consciousness and reduce responsiveness to most stimuli.

## Bedeviled by dust

Dust is a hallmark of summer in many parts of the country. How does it affect your horse's health?

Plain soil dust, rising from range- or cropland, is generally of little consequence. Horses blasted by airborne dirt squinch up their eyes and nostrils to block its entrance. Most of the relatively heavy soil particles that do get inhaled are caught in the mucus of the nasal passages before they reach the lower respiratory tract. So, unless your horse is outside, unsheltered in a serious dust storm, he'll cope well enough with airborne soil particles.

Dust that consists primarily of organic material—manure, molds, pollens, hay and grain fines—may have more serious health consequences. These small, light particles can be pulled into the lungs, where they may trigger allergic responses. Organic dust contributes to the development of heaves, overproduction of airway mucus and other respiratory troubles.

## What makes horses drool?

On an average day, the three pairs of salivary glands in your horse's throat and under his tongue produce 10 gallons of saliva. If the output becomes a river of watery slobber, it's unsightly, but it's nothing to be concerned about in an otherwise healthy horse. In most cases, excessive salivation is a response to chemical irritation. Certain oral dewormers and medications have this effect, but, in the spring and summer, clover contaminated with *Rhizoctonia leguminicola* fungus is the usual trigger of what is commonly called "slobbers." Affected clover is easy to spot: The leaves change from vibrant green to a grayish tinge and eventually turn black. When consumed in moderation, forage infected with this common fungus is harmless, but its bitter taste irritates horses' salivary glands. If you find clover-induced slobbers distasteful, your only recourse is to take your horse off clover-containing pasture until the fall.

When should you be concerned about abnormal drooling? If, in conjunction with excessive salivation, your horse has no appetite, has difficulty swallowing, is feverish and/or looks lethargic, or if the saliva is thick and unusual looking, call your veterinarian to assess the situation.

**TERMINOLOGY**

DYSTOCIA

*Difficult birth. May be due to abnormal size or position of the fetus, inadequate uterine contractions or lack of voluntary exertion by the mare.*

## Waiting for a dewormer to take effect

A new horse comes onto your property, looking a little less thrifty than he should. You decide he could use a thorough deworming. But dewormers don't eliminate their target immediately, and a newcomer added to a herd soon after dosing may still infect others. Droppings from a heavily infested horse can contaminate grass for several feet around each pile, putting other grazers at risk. How long does it take for a dewormer to take effect, and when is it safe to introduce a treated horse into the herd?

Researchers at the University of Kentucky looked into these questions by using an ivermectin treatment for small strongyles—a type of roundworm parasite that commonly infects the intestines of horses after migrating through the digestive tract.

Through a series of fecal egg and larva counts, the researchers determined that isolating horses for three days after treatment significantly minimizes pasture contamination and the exposure of herdmates to parasites. Incomplete development of some larva was noted even before egg counts began to drop, suggesting that ivermectin works on small strongyles immediately. Nonetheless, for peace of mind it's best to wait a few days before adding a previously infested, recently dewormed horse to a herd.

## Diarrhea: causes & cures

A thoroughly unpleasant malady for the folks doing the stall cleaning, diarrhea most often is a transient and harmless condition in the horse. Many foals suffer minor bouts in their first several weeks, and some healthy horses have chronically watery stool.

If your horse begins to defecate more frequently than usual and his stool is loose and watery, keep your eye on his condition, but don't panic: His lower bowel may simply be temporarily flooded with more water than it is capable of absorbing. This could be due to the horse drinking too much water—a nervous habit akin to cribbing—or grazing on moisture-laden pasture. A sudden change in feed also can have a similar effect.

In any event, as long as your horse seems otherwise healthy, diarrhea is less a menace than a nuisance. Over-the-counter antidiarrheal preparations may help foals, but this approach is less practical for grown horses who require far greater doses of the medication. For most cases of minor adult diarrhea, effective treatment involves increasing the horse's grazing time and cutting out his grain ration entirely, if possible. Intestinal irritation—along with the loss of some of the gut's beneficial microflora—may slow recovery, but most horses return to normal in a week or two.

Be on the lookout, however, for signs that your horse's watery feces are the result of a *Red Alert* condition. These include diarrhea that is preceded by or accompanied by fever; comes on violently or with straining; is accompanied by a loss of appetite; produces foul-smelling stool; and/or persists for two weeks or longer and does not respond to the usual treatment. Summon your veterinarian immediately if your horse exhibits any of these signs. They may indicate the presence of infection, endotoxemia, colitis X or another potentially life-threatening ailment.

> **RED ALERT**
>
> DEHYDRATION
>
> *Dehydration occurs when a horse loses body water faster than he can replace it. Left untreated, dehydration can lead to depression, muscle spasms, diarrhea, cardiac arrhythmia, incoordination and death. Seek immediate veterinary assistance if your horse exhibits the following signs:*
>
> * *disorientation, loss of interest in events/surroundings*
> * *dry mucous membranes*
> * *loss of hunger and thirst*
> * *decreased urine output*
> * *muscle spasms.*

## A taste for dirt

Do you frequently catch your horse nibbling on Mother Earth and wonder what you can do to halt the filthy habit?

It could be that his diet lacks essential nutrients, and he's groveling for them in the ground. Or he might have taken up the unclean activity for lack of something better to do. For the most part, dirt eating is not particularly harmful to horses. Yet excessive accumulation of sandy soil in the gut is a common colic cause, and parasite infestation may increase with the earthy intake.

A process of elimination may help you to determine the source of the behavior and, from there, ways to divert the horse from eating dirt

- A lack of salt is probably the most common deficiency behind the habit. Make plain or trace-mineral salt constantly available free choice in your horse's turnout area and/or stall.
- Deficiencies in dietary phosphorus, iron or fiber may be spurring your horse to devour dirt. Consult with your veterinarian about the ration you're currently feeding your horse to see if an upgrade is indicated on any of these accounts.
- Finally, boredom may be behind the problem. Interaction with an active herd and regular training and use will keep your horse in good condition and relieve his tedium, giving him better things to do than gnaw on the ground.

## Preparing a place for delivery

Well before your pregnant mare's expected due date, make sure that you're ready to welcome her foal by preparing the delivery stall. Ideally, it will be at least 14 feet square. It will be well ventilated without any uncomfortable drafts. It also will have good drainage and be as dust-free as possible. Since your expectant mother likely will deliver in the dead of night, make sure all of the nearby light bulbs and electrical outlets are in working order.

Carefully inspect the stall for any hidden hazards. Then clean it out completely, removing all of the bedding and equipment. Scrub the walls and floors with detergent and disinfectant. Before replacing the water buckets and feed tub, thoroughly scrub, disinfect and rinse them clean. (Remember to remove these potentially dangerous extraneous items at delivery time.) Once the floor and walls have completely dried, spread out a thick layer of high-quality straw bedding or clean, resilient rubber matting.

## Signs of an equine earache

When a horse develops an ear infection, the outward signs may include increased sensitivity in the area, frequent head tossing, repeated attempts at rubbing the ear, and the tendency to hold the head at an odd angle with the affected ear low and droopy. A middle-ear infection is often characterized by fever, severe pain and a head tilt. Inner-ear infections, which are rare in horses, usually have strikingly apparent symptoms. Because the inner ear governs a horse's equilibrium, an infection there may cause a loss of coordination and balance.

If your horse exhibits signs of a middle- or inner-ear infection, call your veterinarian without delay. He will likely prescribe antibiotic therapy to combat the problem. For an outer-ear infection, applying a topical remedy will reduce your horse's discomfort and speed healing. In fact, don't be surprised if your veterinarian recommends that you treat your horse's ear infection with the same medication you use for your dog. The regimen involves applying canine ear-cleaning solution to the affected area, letting the horse shake the ear clear and then drying the readily reachable ear surfaces with a soft, clean cloth. Your veterinarian also may prescribe any of several canine ear-infection lotions for you to apply.

> **TERMINOLOGY**
>
> ENTEROLITH
>
> *An abnormal concretion—an intestinal stone—usually formed of mineral salts, in the horse's intestine.*

## Something's in his eye

If a speck of dirt, hay or bedding becomes lodged in your horse's eye, prompt action on your part can help to prevent serious injury and infection.

The indications that something is irritating a horse's eye are obvious. Signs include excessive tearing, squinting, tenderness and sensitivity to light. In addition, his third eyelid (nictitating membrane), located at the inside corner of the eye, may protrude as it tries to cleanse and lubricate the structure.

When you attempt to locate and remove something from your horse's eye, it's best to take a cautious approach, since this is obviously a delicate area and a scratch on the cornea (the outer surface) can open the way for infection. If possible, ask an assistant to restrain your horse while you examine the eye.

If you can see an object on your horse's eye, carefully push up his eyelid with your thumb or first finger and gently remove the material with a cotton swab moistened with sterile saline solution or clean water. If no item is apparent, gently rinse the globe with a flushing syringe full of saline or clean water.

If you are unable to relieve your horse's discomfort, call your veterinarian immediately. He'll check for scratches on the cornea and examine the area for other complications. If the eye is damaged, your veterinarian will likely prescribe topical antibiotics to ward off infection.

Fortunately, the eye is well-equipped to mend itself. Tears contain chemicals and cells that are active in the healing process. And the many tiny blood vessels leading to the cornea a poised to provide a generous blood supply. Barring complications, minor scratches generally take only two to three days to heal.

**AT A GLANCE**

BEFORE AN EMERGENCY

*Along with a list of emergency telephone numbers, post the barn address and written directions to your farm next to each telephone so everyone—even a visitor—can call for help and provide information to emergency personnel.*

## Why your horse needs electrolytes

When your horse sweats, he loses sodium and chloride (which combine to form salt) along with potassium and trace amounts of calcium and magnesium—simple inorganic compounds that are collectively known as electrolytes. These substances dissolve in the horse's body fluids and regulate many chemical processes that occur both in and between the cells. The kidneys are the primary organs involved in regulating electrolyte levels, conserving or excreting the elements as necessary to maintain a stable state of equilibrium (homeostasis) within the horse's body.

For the most part, a balanced diet supplies ample amounts of electrolytes for a moderately worked horse. Grain is high in phosphorus, and legume hays are excellent sources of calcium. The soil in which grain and hay are grown, however, largely determines the feed's mineral content. Your state department of agriculture can provide specific information about locally grown crops, and in many states, it's possible to receive a complete nutritional analysis of your horse feed.

Only if your horse sweats heavily and frequently is he likely to require supplemental electrolytes. Salt is the exception, since horses virtually always need more than they can acquire from grain and hay. Give your horse free access to a trace-mineralized salt block (it isn't advisable to add salt to his feed or water).

He will generally consume no more and no less than his body needs—one half-pound per week is average for an adult horse.

## Exercising the expectant mare

Is exercise safe for your pregnant mare? It's not only safe, it's desirable. Exercise can help a mare process crucial nutrients and deliver them to her developing foal. In addition, the motion resulting from activity encourages proper fetal joint development. And regular exercise can make a mare's eventual foaling easier and safer by toning muscles, combating excessive weight gain and improving general vigor.

For a mare who has been ridden regularly before being bred, there's no reason to stop once she has conceived. But exercise her judiciously and take care not to subject her to too much stress. In general, your mare's fitness level prior to her pregnancy will dictate the intensity and duration of exercise she can sustain during the first eight or nine months she is carrying her foal.

Keep in mind that the stress caused by a sporadic work schedule or a sudden increase in physical demands can have deleterious effects on her health and that of her fetus.

You'll also want to make sure your mare is receiving adequate nutrition to support her additional energy needs. Increase the concentrate portion of her feed ration as follows:
- one pound per hour of easy moving
- two pounds per hour of work producing some sweating
- three pounds per hour of work producing a good lather
- five pounds per hour of maximal effort (which is rarely sustained for more than a few minutes at a time).

Also, make sure that the supplemental feed contains sufficient levels of calcium and phosphorus (0.5 to 0.7 percent each).

When your mare reaches the eighth or ninth month of gestation, the weight of the fetus and its demand for nutrients become substantial. At this point, begin tapering off the mare's exercise—asking for no more than a walk or an easy jog—but continue regular pasture turnout.

Once your mare delivers her foal, resume her exercise program gradually. In general, you can begin longeing your mare about a week after the foal arrives. Most mares are ready for regular riding about a month after foaling—but remember to consider the foal's safety.

## Be prepared for an emergency on the road

Most trailer trips are uneventful, but a mechanical breakdown, equine injury or accident can happen on even the shortest jaunts. So before you hit the road, gather these essential items for use in an emergency:

- gloves to protect your hands and provide a better grip
- a sharp knife to free entangled horses
- a sturdy rope, at least eight feet long, with a heavy-duty snap to use as a lead, a towrope or even a pulley
- nylon halters for restraining horses who may have broken their shipping halters
- a well-stocked first-aid kit
- extra hay to occupy the horses while you resolve a crisis
- a separate lug wrench specifically for your trailer wheels and a jack or block ramp to use in changing a flat tire
- cash.

To test your emergency preparedness, load a horse or two in your trailer and go through the tire-changing routine as though you were actually stranded on the side of the road. Check all the lug nuts to make sure you can loosen them. You may need to multiply your leverage by adding a pipe extension to your lug wrench.

## When he won't eat

A horse who isn't interested in eating is a rare creature indeed. But you may have one in your barn who's simply a finicky eater. Once a thorough veterinary examination has ruled out ill health or bad teeth as the cause of a lack of appetite, take a look at your horse's feeding circumstances to see if they may be contributing to his disinterest.

- *He's overwhelmed.* A large serving of grain could be too much for your horse to consume comfortably. Dole out multiple small meals—as many as six, if your schedule allows—to a horse who needs every grain to keep him in condition. An automatic feeder that dispenses grain a handful at a time would relieve you of the duty, while still giving the horse all he's interested in eating at any one time.
- *He's distracted.* The kicking, pawing and vocalizing that often accompany feeding time in a large barn can be too exciting for some horses. Feeding a finicky eater in a quiet, remote area may provide the calm he needs to focus on his grain.
- *He's lonely.* Leaving a slow eater alone in the barn to finish his meal can backfire when separation anxieties take hold. Delay turnout for a few buddies in adjoining stalls, keeping them content with hay, so the slowpoke has company.
- *He's bored.* Plain or pelleted grain may not be enough to tempt the taste buds of a picky horse. Make a gradual change to a more delectable meal, such as sweet feed or oats, or garnish his normal rations with molasses or applesauce.
- *He doesn't like the presentation.* Some really picky horses prefer grain served in just one way. You may have to experiment with different feeders and placements. Start out with more "natural" arrangements, such as grain spread in a thin layer in a shallow trough.

## Fever facts

You can't put a hand to your horse's forehead to detect a fever, but being able to monitor his core temperature (most likely with a rectal thermometer) is a basic skill of good horsekeeping. Horses' body temperatures vary much more than ours do. Any reading between 99.5 and 101.5 degrees Fahrenheit can be considered normal, depending on the individual horse, the time of day and nearby air temperature. Determine your horse's "normal" temperature when he's healthy and following his usual routine by taking readings two or three times a day at set times over the course of several days. This baseline information will help you evaluate the relative abnormality of thermometer readings you take later when he is ill.

If your horse's temperature is above his personal norm, but he's showing no other signs of sickness, take another reading in the evening, when the air has cooled. If the second reading is still above normal, an illness may be brewing. Keep an eye out for developing signs, such as coughing or diarrhea.

Most fevers are caused by bacterial or viral infections. The body raises its internal temperature to 103 degrees or higher to help to kill the pathogens. Rhinopneumonitis and influenza viruses can cause temperature spikes to nearly 105 degrees before any outward signs of illness appear. Consult your veterinarian about feverish ailments and episodes, and direct your nursing efforts toward treating the cause rather than specifically fighting fever.

Fever itself is unlikely to harm a horse until it reaches 106 or 107 degrees, at which point it is classified as heatstroke. Exercise in hot and humid conditions is the usual cause of such extremes in body temperature, but a few illnesses, such as Potomac horse fever, also can produce life-threatening fevers. Use cool-water hosing of the neck and legs, along with ice packs under the tail and around the head, to lower body temperatures as quickly as possible while the veterinarian is summoned.

## Built-in fly control

During fly season, when most people are spraying repellents, hanging fly strips and wielding swatters, horses are making use of their own built-in insect-control apparatus. In addition to his mane and tail, the horse has a specialized muscle group called the "fly shaker" to help him get rid of insects, dust and other surface irritants. A horse's face, neck, chest, forearms (on the outside), shoulders, barrel and flanks benefit from the fly-shaker muscle, which compels pests to disembark through semi-voluntary contractions that "shake" the skin.

The fly shaker is found within the hypodermis, the deepest layer of a horse's skin. A stretchy network of loosely arranged fibrous tissue and muscle sheets, the hypodermis slides freely over most underlying muscles and bones, except in a few places—at the hips and backbone—where it is attached to structures beneath. Upon stimulation by a fly or some other irritant, the fly shaker muscle contracts within the hypodermis, producing a twitchlike wrinkling of the horse's skin.

It's important to distinguish between fly-shaker action and muscle spasms caused by pain or emotional distress. Fly-shaker motion causes only the skin to move. With muscle spasms, a horse's posture changes and the deeper, underlying muscle mass moves.

## Controlling the frenzied feeder

Bolting feed is more than bad manners: Horses who eat too fast are at higher risk for a number of problems, including improper digestion, "choke" and colic. And while the classic cure of putting rocks in the feed bucket may slow a feed bolter somewhat, it won't solve the problem. A particularly crafty horse can find a way to push rocks aside or remove them. Try these four techniques for slowing greedy eaters:

1. Feed small amounts of grain several times a day rather than one or two large feedings.
2. Spread the feed thinly in a large trough so the horse can get only a small amount with each bite.
3. Feed hay before grain to take the edge off the horse's appetite.
4. Add a layer of hay on top of grain so the horse must burrow and thus inadvertently ingest hay, which dilutes the concentrated energy in his meal.

## Footing's effect on conditioning

One of the more frustrating aspects of riding is that it seems when you finally get suitable weather, the ground underfoot resembles either mush or concrete. And if you don't have the luxury of an indoor arena, it may seem an impossible task to keep your horse fit. But there are ways to work around not-so-ideal footing conditions without jeopardizing your horse's soundness.

*When the ground is hard,* it's best to slow the pace of your sessions. (Now is a good time to work on improving your horse's walk.) Excessive work on hard ground creates concussion for a horse's bones. You can ensure that your horse is still investing the same effort and increasing his fitness—even if he's not moving as quickly—by working him on steeper grades.

If you don't have hills to work on, then go for distance. Do all of your sharp work near the end of the session when your horse is less likely to become overexcited and you'll decrease his chances of injuring himself on hard ground.

*When the ground is too soft,* your horse risks muscle and tendon injury. Perhaps it's a good time to take him swimming or go for a hack along gravel roads or highway verges. They may still be firm enough. In fact, gravel is at its best when it has been wet down.

If neither of these options is available, try conditioning your horse using interval training methods—controlled speed works of precise distances separated by controlled relief exercise, allowing partial recovery of the horse's resting pulse. Short spurts on the best footing you can find may equal longer fast canters or lopes. Be sure to follow your horse's pulse to anticipate fatigue. Deep footing and soft ground can easily tire a working horse.

**VITAL STATISTICS**

READY TO NURSE

• *Most foals stand and nurse within the first hour of birth, although some take longer.*

• *Expect your foal to nurse frequently in the days following his arrival— three to seven times per hour.*

## Facing a fracture

A broken bone is one of the most serious injuries a horse can sustain, but advances in veterinary orthopedics and surgery have improved the chances for a successful recovery. The prognosis depends on the nature of the injury—the type of break, its location and the extent of the tissue damage. Fractures fall into five general categories. From the least serious break to the most severe complication, they include:

- *a crack*—an unseparated fracture in which the bone has not actually been split into two or more distinct parts.
- *simple fracture*—a single break that leaves two pieces of bone.
- *comminuted fracture*—a bone that has been broken or crushed into small pieces.
- *multiple fracture*—two or more bones are broken, or a bone is broken in two or more places.
- *compound fracture*—the skin has been broken, and the affected bone ends are exposed or contaminated.

Generally, the higher up on a horse's leg a fracture occurs, the more serious it is. For example, treating a break in the horse's radius—the principle bone of the forearm—can be extremely difficult because it plays a significant role in weight bearing and is surrounded by quite a lot of muscle that can permit the bone ends to move, disrupting healing. In fact, separated fractures above the knee or hock are frequently catastrophic, and many are hopeless. In contrast, a horse with a comparable fracture lower in the leg has a much better chance of surviving his injury and perhaps even someday returning to work.

In some cases, the soft-tissue damage that accompanies a fracture causes more problems than the actual break since injuries to joints, ligaments and tendons can be slow to heal.

Depending on the severity of the break, the signs that a horse has suffered a fracture range from subtle (a slight limp) to alarming (a dangling, deformed limb). In any case, if you suspect that your horse has fractured a bone, call your veterinarian immediately. Prompt attention is critical to the animal's recovery.

## A moist frog is a healthy frog

That triangular wedge of padding in your horse's sole, with its dark gray color, roughened surface and usual coating of dung and debris, is never a pretty sight. But pretty is as pretty does, and the frog is essential to locomotion, absorbing concussion with every step.

Oil glands within the frog keep it pliable, a necessary quality of any shock absorber. A healthy frog has the consistency of a hard rubber eraser. You can feel it give when you push firmly with your thumb. If glandular oils can't keep up with environmental conditions, however, the frog may dry out and lose its pliability. A dry frog is very hard and may appear smaller and more "shriveled" than normal.

Dryness also can cause superficial cracks in the frog. These are no cause for concern as long as they're less than a quarter-inch deep. Bleeding cracks are a sign of desperate dryness. Daily application of an over-the-counter hoof dressing, or a greasy concoction like petroleum jelly or pine tar mixed with glycerin, may help preserve the natural moisture balance.

## Ease his fear of fly spray

Have a horse who reacts violently to the noise or sensation of being sprayed with insecticide? Here are four steps for easing his fear:

1. *Use a good-quality, quiet sprayer.* Pump sprayers that must be "primed" first produce their mist in near silence.

2. *Control your body language.* Approach the horse at his shoulder, use the spray bottle in slow rhythmic sweeps, and respect the horse's "threat" zones (his head and hindquarters).

3. *Acclimatize your horse to the noise.* Fill the sprayer with water and stand outside your horse's stall while he eats. Spray at regular intervals, pointing away from your horse, until he ignores the noise in favor of food.

Repeat the process inside the stall—again without actually spraying the horse. A few sessions of dinnertime spraying should reduce his terror. In fact, the association with food may even make spray sounds welcome.

4. *Desensitize your horse to the spray.* Once noise is no longer a problem, find the level of spray contact your horse will tolerate. Start with a gentle mist, still using plain water. Pull the trigger slowly, and aim the spray at his shoulder. If even this sensation is intolerable for your supersensitive horse, you can flick water gently at him with your fingers first. When he accepts this, reintroduce the light spray. Continue at a base comfort level until he ignores the misting, and then increase the pressure of the spray.

Move to other areas of the body as your horse accepts spraying at each site and intensity. Whenever he objects, return to the previously acceptable level until he settles, and then try again.

## Why foals eat feces

The habit of eating feces—technically known as coprophagy—is common among young foals. In fact, it is considered a normal stage of a foal's development, thought to be brought on partly by curiosity as youngsters seek to discover what is edible and partly by physiological need: Some researchers think foals eat feces to populate their guts with the microorganisms they need to switch from a milk to a forage diet.

Foals usually eat only fresh manure from their dams. By avoiding aged droppings, the foal limits his risk of parasite infection. No matter how distasteful it may seem, a youngster's brief fling with coprophagy, usually during the first weeks of life, is no need for concern.

## The birth of a flake

We all know that those handy sections of hay referred to as "flakes" make doling out rations easier, but just how does a pile of loose hay become a flake? Flakes are formed through a repeating cycle of compression and release in a baling machine. The baler picks up a continuous "windrow" of hay from the ground and moves it into the bale chamber. As the plunger moves back and forth, the incoming forage is cut and then compressed, forming a flake. The flake is then pushed against the resistance of the baling twine and the two to three most recently made bales. Successive strokes make subsequent flakes until the preset bale length is accumulated and tied off. Successive bales push their predecessors out. The density of the windrow and the speed of the tractor determine the thickness of each flake, which does not necessarily reflect the quality of the hay.

## Feed-room renovation

If your feed room serves as both kitchen and pharmacy for your horses, you'll find at least one item on the following list helpful for meeting these purposes more efficiently:

- a rodent-proof, horse-proof feed bin. (A recycled chest-type freezer, with motor and latch removed, works well.)
- hot and cold running water for dampening feeds, making bran mashes and scrubbing equipment.
- a large chalkboard or marker board with every horse's ration listed on it. (With this information, plus stall or halter nameplates, anyone can feed in case of emergency.)
- a mortar and pestle or a coffee-bean grinder for pulverizing pills.
- an economy-sized jug of corn oil with a pump dispenser.
- a hanging scale, with a bowl and a hook for weighing feed and hay.
- a mini-refrigerator, for storing perishable medications and "mixers," such as applesauce.
- small, airtight, plastic containers to hold a week's worth of premeasured daily supplements.
- a cat or terrier who lives to kill mice.

## Forging: the sound of tapping toes

Click, click, click—a metallic symphony announces the arrival of a horse who "forges." A horse is said to forge when his hind toe strikes the bottom of his front shoe or hoof, usually at the trot. Shod hooves produce a distinct "clink" as the two shoes strike; unshod horses produce, if anything, a dull "clunk." Contrary to popular belief, forging horses will not trip themselves or pull off their shoes; more often this is caused by overreaching, when the hind toe strikes the front *heels*. Forging causes only a premature wearing of the toes of shoes.

Short-backed, long-legged horses are more likely to forge, as are those in need of a trim—low heels cause the forefoot to remain down just long enough for long hind hooves to catch the bottom. A horse who is "on the forehand" or not "on the aids" may also forge as he pushes a heavy front end around the ring. Forging may be the first indication of fatigue or may signal a chronically lazy mover.

A combination of shoeing and riding adjustments can cure forging. Asking a horse for collection will compel him to "pick up" his front end and keep him alert and stepping quickly. In addition, your farrier can "quicken" the front feet and "slow" the hind by raising the front heels and lowering the back ones.

## The telltale gums

Your horse seems slightly ill, but you're not sure why. As you check his vital signs, don't overlook the inside of his mouth. Taking a quick look at his gums—noting their color and circulation—can provide valuable clues to what the problem may be.

**Color:** In healthy horses, gums are pale pink in color, although they may turn a slightly brighter pink from the increased circulation of exercise. Pale, almost-white gums are a sign of anemia or internal hemorrhage. Brick-red or purple gums may indicate poisoning, a *Red Alert* situation, requiring a veterinarian's immediate attention.

**Circulation:** Another way gums indicate health is through capillary refill time (CRT)—the amount of time it takes for blood to return to the gums after pressure is applied. To find your horse's CRT, press your thumb firmly against his gum above an upper corner incisor. Hold the pressure for a few seconds and then release. Note how long it takes for the pink color to return to that spot. A healthy horse's CRT is normally one to two seconds. Color that returns faster reflects increased circulation, perhaps from exercise or excitement. Color that returns much slower can indicate the slowed circulation of shock, illness or anemia. If your horse's CRT seems slow and he shows any other signs of illness, consult your veterinarian.

## Grooming tools & horse health

Though inexpensive, your grooming tools play an important role in maintaining your horse's health. They deserve the same level of care you give the rest of your equipment:

- ***Keep everything clean.*** Prevent dirt buildup on brushes during grooming by swiping them across a currycomb every few strokes. For deeper cleaning every few months, vacuum brush bristles down to the roots and dip all items in a disinfectant solution. (Five parts water to one part chlorine bleach works well.) Dry them in the sun, if possible.
- ***Share grooming equipment with care.*** Brushes are an ideal means of spreading skin disease from horse to horse. If a particular horse's skin looks iffy, assemble a separate grooming kit exclusively for use on him, and disinfect it often.
- ***Store tools protectively.*** The perfect container for your grooming kit is one that wards off dust, chaff, mold and chewing dogs or other animals. A sturdy plastic carrier with a secure lid works well. Arrange your stored brushes so their bristles won't be flattened by their own weight or by pressure from other grooming tools. A good technique is to press two brushes together to interlock their bristles for unsmashed storage.

**TERMINOLOGY**

GALL

*A sore on the skin caused by the chafing of tack.*

## Why not get him a goat?

Most horses probably prefer to live exclusively with other horses, but if your farm-management practices necessitate interspecies pasture use, consider health factors, grazing habits and personality conflicts when you're looking to find your horse a "roomie."

Goats and horses can forge enduring bonds when sharing living space. Goats thrive on plants that horses find inedible, including honeysuckle and other vines, so there is no competition for forage. Fences have to be secure to keep in these skilled climbers and crawlers (diamond mesh is both impenetrable for them and safe for your horse), and uncastrated males can be smelly. On the whole, however, goats make great pasturemates for horses.

## Girth fit checklist

Your horse is saying he needs a different girth or kinder application when he
- cow kicks or lashes around with his head as you cinch him up
- "blows up" when you girth him (actually, he's tensing his chest muscles to brace his rib cage against the pressure)
- groans
- rears over backwards
- takes mincing steps when first asked to move off.

Not all such responses are commentary on the girth and girthing process, however. Your lashing, groaning, rearing, mincing horse may instead be telling you that his ill-fitting saddle is just about killing his withers or back. You can distinguish the source of his aggravation quite simply. Mount up. Your weight will decrease girth strain and add to saddle pain. If the horse's reaction subsides, the girth is the likely culprit; if it persists or gets worse, the saddle is the source.

Correcting the problem may not eliminate what often becomes a habitual response, however.

Unless you can see or feel damage to the skin or underlying muscle, the negative response on being girthed is probably the result of simple sensitivity. Yes, some horses are quite ticklish, so pity the poor beast, remembering how you'd react if someone were poking or pinching your underarm area. For that hypersensitive horse, choose a girth with a soft contact surface, and tighten it ever so gradually, walking the horse a few steps between each increment. Otherwise, each riding session begins with torment—hardly the association you want your horse to make with mounted work.

## What's the role of the guttural pouches?

Two large, air-filled sacs, the horse's guttural pouches branch off from the eustachian tubes, which extend from the pharynx to the middle ear. Roughly the size and shape of a human hand, the pouches are positioned symmetrically on either side of the horse's head.

Some anatomists think the guttural pouches assist the eustachian tubes in equalizing pressure in the middle ear. Others believe the pouches are necessary to respiration. Still others believe they evolved to facilitate swallowing.

Most problems with the guttural pouches are caused by infections. Signs include thick nasal discharge or blood from one nostril, sometimes with swallowing difficulty and limited range of motion of the head. During pneumonia and diseases such as strangles (a *Streptococcus equi* infection), the guttural pouches can fill with pus, making it difficult for the horse to swallow. Also, as a secondary effect of strangles, small pebblelike masses called chondroids can remain in the pouches and harbor bacteria for years. Guttural-pouch mycosis, in which the arteries in the pouch wall are invaded by fungi, can be fatal if the arteries burst.

## A strategy for feeding spring grass

After a winter of feeding hay, most horse owners rejoice at the sight of the first blades of grass appearing in the pasture. But just how beneficial is the first forage of the season?

Spring grass, which tends to come in very quickly, is higher in water content and lower in fiber than dry summer grass. Horses who consume the new growth in quantity are likely to experience watery stools. The actual nutritional benefits of emerging grass, as well as its energy content, are significantly lower than those of later grasses. Spring grass also has a higher protein content than other grasses, which is good for lactating mares but can spell trouble for other horses. When an animal accustomed to a relatively dense winter diet suddenly consumes watery, lower-fiber, high-protein feed, the resulting shock to the intestinal microflora may lead to enteritis or colic.

This does not mean, however, that your horse must be forbidden from grazing succulent spring pastures. As long as he has other roughage—be it remaining older growth surviving the winter or some clean hay—to complement the younger grass, he'll generally find the right balance.

## Go galloping

The highlight of many a fair-weather trail ride is a gallop, with your horse moving so fast the surroundings become a blur. But beyond the sheer fun factor, work at full speed has many benefits for both horse and rider.

The reach and intensity of brisk gallop strides can dramatically improve the horse's other gaits, especially those that have become short, choppy and lackluster from too many laps around the ring. In addition, the balance required by a galloping horse carries over to other gaits, making him more sure-footed and confident. Galloping also provides a good cardiovascular workout and opens up the airways. In fact, horses with heaves actually breathe better after a brief run. Speed does involve risk, however, so don't gallop a horse with a heart condition, serious structural shortcomings or a tendency to bolt.

Galloping can boost the skill and confidence levels of riders, too, but only if they are well prepared. Before hitting the road, practice the galloping or two-point position: Stand in the stirrups with your weight over your lower legs and lowered heels. With your seat about four inches from the saddle, tip your upper body slightly forward, but don't depend on the horse's neck for balance. When you can maintain this position without falling forward or backward through the walk, trot and canter, you're ready to go galloping. If you are inexperienced at riding an all-out run, follow these galloping tips:

- Shorten your stirrups about two inches to give yourself more security and make the two-point position less fatiguing.
- Hold onto a neck strap. A stirrup leather buckled around your horse's neck serves as a handle, preserving his mouth if the ride gets bumpy.
- After a good warm-up, head for an area with familiar, uncomplicated terrain: A broad, smooth stretch of trail heading slightly uphill is ideal, as the incline will help you slow to a stop.
- Pick up an easy canter or lope ("shotgunning" into the gallop encourages bolting). Then, when all is well, get into your galloping position, grab the neck strap and urge your horse on.
- When you are ready to pull up, sit back down in the saddle. Bring your shoulders back over your hips, deaden your hands and sit against the motion. Do not pull on the reins. Most horses are influenced much more by this change in position than even the most severe rein aids.
- Vary the location and duration of your gallops so your horse doesn't become "hot" in anticipation of a run at a particular spot.

## Health clues in the stall

You can gather telling clues about a horse's health and habits by taking a look around his stall.

*First, check out the walls.* Hock-high horizontal scrapes along a wall are the calling card of a kicker. Crescent-shaped scrapes higher up may be remnants of a cast horse's struggle to rise. Vertical scrapes at head height are left behind from the frantic tooth dragging and wall biting of an impatient horse at feeding time. A dock-height waxy area with a tail hair or two caught on the wall indicates a rear-end rubber. Horizontal boards that look as if a beaver has been snacking on them come courtesy of a wood chewer. Those that look mashed smooth by a hammer are the handiwork of a cribber.

*Inspect what's underfoot.* The appearance of manure gives clues to the occupant's digestive health, and churned-up bedding can indicate colicky behavior. Keep an eye out for rearrangement of the footing: Horses with navicular disease often make small piles of bedding to elevate their own heels.

*Dig beneath the bedding for more clues.* A crater in front of the feed bin gives away a mealtime pawer, a worn path in front of the door is left behind by a weaver, and a circular track around the entire stall is the mark of a stall walker. A sopping wet floor under the water bucket indicates not only boredom-induced playing but possibly troubles in food chewing and swallowing.

## 4 ways to fortify shelly hooves

Your farrier has done an excellent job of fortifying your horse's weak, shelly hooves, but what happens to them between farrier visits can go a long way toward preserving their health.

1. *Keep your horse's hooves as dry as possible.* Excessive moisture weakens hoof walls and provides an ideal environment for bacterial invasions. Just as destructive as excess moisture, however, are extreme fluctuations between wet and dry conditions, which cause the hoof to expand and contract with each moisture change. Horses on summer pasture go through the wet-dry cycle daily, with morning dew giving way to ground-baking dryness. Frequent baths and postexercise hosings also contribute to this problem, so stick to careful spongings that keep hooves relatively dry.

2. *Stand your horse on solid ground.* A tenderfooted horse may look ouchy on harder footing, but the firm ground helps toughen his feet. An ideal flooring for stabled horses is made up of dense stall mats covered by a thin layer of dry bedding.

3. *Make sure your horse gets enough exercise.* Simply walking around a pasture stimulates hoof circulation and growth. Even if your mount's feet look fragile, resist the urge to restrict his activities.

4. *Apply hoof tougheners.* Commercial bonding agents formulated to harden horses' hooves are available through tack stores. Ask your farrier which ones would be most suitable for your horse. It's best to avoid preparations that contain oils because they can contribute to softening of the hoof wall.

## The anatomy of the hock

The hock is the strongest joint of its size in the horse's body. A complex arrangement of bones, ligaments and tendons allows the hock to fulfill two demanding functions: multiplying propulsion through leverage and bearing weight when it is partially flexed.

The hock is much like the human ankle, but it doesn't have the same capacity for moving from side to side (laterally). However, it is extremely flexible as a hinge. Its huge range of motion approaches 160 degrees. To enable the stifle joints to pass outside the horse's belly when he trots and gallops, the hinging motion of the hock is slightly turned to the outside.

In the hock, 10 bones come together to form four joints, but only the joint between the gaskin bone and the uppermost (tibial tarsal) hock bone is moveable. The others are bound and virtually immobilized by very strong ligaments. This complex array of small bones and nearly motionless joints allows the hock to sustain concussion better than a single bone mass could.

Despite their lack of motion, however the lower joints of the hock experience the most disease and lameness (arthritis). However, arthritis can "burn out" and seal these joints, with a painless outcome.

**TERMINOLOGY**

**HEAVES**

*Forced expiratory effort in horses due to narrowing of the small airways of the lungs. The condition also is known as chronic obstructive pulmonary disease (COPD).*

## Healthy horse, healthy hair

Whoever said beauty is only skin deep obviously wasn't speaking of horses. The glow from a healthy horse's coat does, in fact, radiate from within. So, if your horse is looking less than lustrous, consider some beauty-enhancing management changes.

- **General health.** If a depressed appetite or lethargic behavior accompanies a dull coat, it's a good bet something other than a lack of grooming is bothering your horse. Consult with your veterinarian. Your horse may have parasites, allergies, an infection or other ills.
- **Diet.** Balanced rations comprised of quality feeds and forage are the best shine enhancers for horses. A supplemental drizzle of oil (corn, linseed, soybean or canola) on the grain ration can help increase coat glossiness, as can biotin, a B-complex vitamin.
- **Grooming.** Shampooing not only removes the grime from a horse's coat, it also strips the natural oil, called sebum, that supplies the built-in shine. Hold off on repeated washings in the spring, and vigorously hand groom your horse each day to remove dirt and redistribute sebum.
- **Clipping.** Body clipping also shortcuts the shine for a few weeks, as light doesn't reflect off the blunt ends of cut hairs. Instead of clipping, speed shedding naturally using a currycomb and elbow grease.
- **Turnout.** The fresh air and activity of outdoor living will not only improve your horse's overall health and attitude but perk up his coat as well. The sun and bugs may damage the hair somewhat, but rolls in the grass are nature's best coat buffers.

## Why don't his hooves match?

If a horse's hooves have been two different sizes for as long as you've known him, but this doesn't seem to be causing any soundness or performance problems, don't worry and don't try to "fix" it, especially just for appearance's sake. If, however, the difference limits him significantly, invest in a veterinary workup to discover the cause of the problem and correct it when possible. Have your farrier trim the feet with their unique structure in mind. His job is not to force the hooves to look the same but to try not to let their differences become more marked over time. In general, the larger hoof is probably the "normal"-sized one. The smaller hoof may be caused by

- inborn conformation
- developmental orthopedic disease
- disuse of the foot due to injury or soreness, which leads to atrophy and shrinkage
- a habitual grazing posture by the horse in which the same forefoot is kept forward, making it larger and lower-heeled, and the other is held back, making it smaller and higher-heeled

- a consistent difference in the way the farrier has trimmed the two hooves over time.

A horse with uneven feet may favor the smaller-hooved leg slightly by refusing to pick up that lead or being slightly "off" when circling in that direction. In some "working sound" individuals, the larger hoof may get tender from long, hard work.

## Handling heat and humidity

Weathermen call it the "misery index" to indicate how heat and humidity work together to make you feel sticky and gross in the dog days of summer. But does your horse feel just as miserable as you do in steamy weather?

Scientific research involving Olympic-caliber equine athletes showed that high humidity does not begin to affect horses' cooling abilities adversely until temperatures reach about 75 degrees. At lower temperatures, horses remain fairly comfortable, even when there is a lot of moisture in the air. But when temperature and humidity climb together, horses are no longer able to cool themselves as effectively.

The horse is the only domestic animal that dissipates heat through body-wide sweating. The evaporation of sweat pulls the heat from blood and tissue out through the skin. The amount of moisture in the air affects the rate of evaporation and thus the degree of relief your horse experiences. In high-desert areas, where humidity is as low as 10 percent, evaporation is rapid, and sweating cools a horse quickly at high, as well as more moderate, temperatures. At the other atmospheric extreme, 100 percent humidity, no evaporation occurs, leaving the sweating horse as hot as ever.

So just how does your horse feel on an 85-degree day with 90 percent humidity? You be the judge: With your exposed skin and higher surface-to-weight ratio, your cooling capacities in hot, muggy weather are more efficient than your horse's. If you feel sticky and oppressed, your horse feels even worse.

You can minimize the misery with two simple precautions:

***Body clip your horse.*** Yes, break out the clippers before summer sets in and repeat whenever the hair grows to one-half inch or longer. Evaporation takes place closer to the skin on the clipped coat, providing more relief than when it occurs on the end of a longer hair shaft.

***Ride him wet.*** If you must work your horse on a hot, muggy day, skip the preride grooming. Instead, hose him off with cool water. The cool-water rinse takes up body heat, delaying and suppressing the sweating response and conserving critical internal-water reserves and electrolytes. If your horse dries out or starts to sweat heavily before the ride is over, douse him again. And fret not. Riding a clean, wet horse won't cause skin irritation under the tack. To help post-ride cooling, repeatedly wet him down and scrape away the excess—an essential step, since water left pooled on the surface actually holds heat.

## 10 reasons to love ichthammol

Messy, smelly and downright gross, ichthammol may not be your first choice for treating your horse, but you can't best its versatility and affordability. The sticky ointment reduces inflammation, draws out infection, kills germs and soothes pain. Here are 10 reasons to reach for ichthammol:

1. Pack it around and over draining hoof punctures to draw out pus.
2. Use it to coax "gravels" to burst at the coronary band.
3. Slather it on a case of scratches, and cover the pastern with a sock or shipping boot. Within a day, the scabs come off easily and painlessly. For crusty cases, put plastic wrap over the ichthammol to hold in the heat.
4. Cover a rainrot-riddled back and rump with ichthammol to soften the scabs and kill the bacterial agent. A soapy bath a few days later removes the ichthammol and loosened crusts.
5. Clear up "saddle acne" overnight with a spot of ichthammol on each "pimple."
6. Coat minor cuts and abrasions to minimize pain and protect from infection.
7. Rub it on the muzzle to take the sting out

### TERMINOLOGY

**INFLAMMATION**
*The body's response to injury that is marked by capillary dilation, redness, heat and pain. Inflammation removes harmful bacteria and damaged tissue and initiates the healing process.*

of sunburn on a light-skinned nose. But don't expect the dark goo to prevent a recurrence. Ichthammol is not a sunscreen.

**8.** Ease the painful effects of photosensitivity with a coating on scabs and raw skin. Plastic wrap and bandages over the ichthammol accelerate the benefits to affected lower legs.

**9.** Work a teaspoon or so of greasy ichthammol onto the dock of the tail to repel ticks for as long as two weeks.

**10.** Relieve the maddening itch of insect bites with ichthammol. The persistent goo wards off further feasts as well, particularly along the crest of the neck and on the midline of the belly.

## Relief for itchy skin

Topical treatments can give your itchy horse some relief, even if they don't cure the problem. Therapeutic shampoos, dips and rinses available from veterinarians and pet/animal-supply houses incorporate the following active ingredients:

- *iodine*—for infectious conditions, including ringworm and secondary bacterial infections.
- *lime sulfur*—for fungal infections and mange-mite infestations.
- *chlorhexidine*—for fungal and secondary bacterial infections.
- *benzoyl peroxide*—for fungal and secondary bacterial infections.
- *tar*—for controlling dandruff/scaling (seborrhea) and associated itch.
- *sulfur*, combined with tar or salicylic acid—for controlling microbial action, dandruff/scaling and itch.
- *colloidal oatmeal,* alone or combined with an antihistamine, hydrocortisone or anesthetic—to reduce itch.

*Hypoallergenic animal shampoos* that are formulated without soap are useful for cleaning the already irritated surface of equine itch victims. Subsequent application of *skin moisturizers*—in rinse, spray or gel form—can reduce the discomfort further. Finally, over-the-counter *glucocorticoid ointments* and *anti-itch lotions* may provide temporary relief for inflammation caused by insect bites or plant irritants.

**VITAL STATISTICS**

IRON

- Iron is critical to a horse's endurance potential because it is used in oxygen transport and hemoglobin production.
- Iron is found in most forages and grains, in ample amounts for horses in all stages of work and development.

## Avoiding impaction

To minimize your horse's risk of developing impaction colic, take these precautions:

- Have your horse's teeth checked regularly and floated as needed to correct uneven tooth wear.
- Provide fine-stemmed hay, especially if your horse is elderly.
- Deworm your horse on a regular schedule.
- Encourage your horse to drink enough water. Refill his water bucket every morning and evening, noting how much he has consumed. In cold weather, use an insulated bucket to prevent freezing.
- To encourage exercise, keep your horse turned out as much as possible, preferably with or near other horses. If he's mainly kept in a stall, schedule one or more periods of exercise and turnout daily.

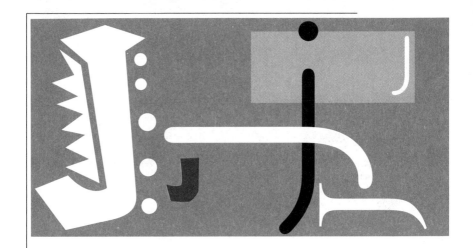

## The source of jaundiced gums

When your horse's gums lose their healthy pink color and take on a yellowish tint, it's usually a sign that something's amiss. The source of the trouble could be as minor and as easy to rectify as a disrupted feeding schedule, or as irreversible and fatal as liver disease. In any case, jaundiced gums are evidence of trouble within, and the more intense their hue, the more serious the condition.

A few day's deprivation of feed is the most common cause of yellow gums in horses. Without an adequate supply of nutrients, the horse's liver isn't able to convert the substance bilirubin into bile during digestion. Yellow-orange in color, bilirubin is left behind when red blood cells die and decompose—a normal and never-ending process. When the level of bilirubin in the blood gets high enough, the horse's gums and the lining of his eyelids show the telltale yellow color, which can range from pale lemon to bright mustard. There is little cause for alarm if a horse who's off his feed develops jaundiced gums, as long as you can identify why his appetite isn't up to par and get him eating again.

Instances when yellow gums signal a different and far more dangerous condition include excessive red-blood-cell destruction (hemolysis) and liver disease.

In the case of hemolytic jaundice, the excess bilirubin accumulates as large numbers of red blood cells rapidly die. Treatment depends on the condition's cause. Horses can develop hemolytic jaundice for a variety of reasons. For example, the

## AT A GLANCE

JOINT FACTS

*Equine joints come in three varieties:*

- *syndesmoses, in which bones are linked by ligaments*
- *synchondroses, in which bones are linked by cartilage*
- *synovial joints, in which cartilage-coated bone ends are completely separate and the space between them is encapsulated in a fluid-filled membrane.*

gums may turn yellow after a horse ingests the chemical phenothiazine or becomes infected with the virus that causes equine infectious anemia (EIA).

A far more life-threatening source of jaundice is liver failure. Usually by the time this problem becomes apparent, the organ's function is so critically impaired that it is too late to save the horse's life.

## Why do joints click?

Clicking in horse's joints occurs mostly in the fetlocks and less often in the hocks. The former has a higher, sharper sound. In "clickers," the rolling of the fibers of the main collateral ligaments is not smooth during flexion and extension, causing the snapping sound. This is a painless, harmless condition and should not be a source of worry.

## Just plain jumpy

If you've ever ridden a horse who's a bundle of nerves, you know that equine anxiety is a serious matter. If allowed to build unchecked, it exacts a heavy toll on a horse's ability to perform. It also jeopardizes his health and soundness. In the short term, an anxious horse is likely to tire more quickly during work sessions and will find it difficult to concentrate on your requests and instruction. Over time, however, he may become more susceptible to digestive upset and more prone to injury, since taut muscles and tendons tear more easily than loose, pliant ones.

## TERMINOLOGY

JUGULAR VEINS

*The large veins located on either side of the horse's windpipe in the underside of the neck. They carry blood from the head and neck to the chest.*

How can you defuse these destructive processes and calm your jumpy horse? Consider these three possibilities:

1. **pain or discomfort.** Ill-fitting equipment, as well as stiffness or muscle soreness, can render even a normally laid-back horse fearful, tense and short-tempered.

2. **nervous handling.** Because he is very sensitive to human body language, a horse's mood or disposition often reflects that of his handler or rider. Inconsistency is another culprit. A rider who fails to direct his horse's motion with the same set of clear, precisely delivered cues will only confuse and frustrate his mount.

3. **an unsettling environment.** Restrictive stabling conditions that allow a horse just an hour or two of liberty a day, and crowded social arrangements that require him to fight for his feed and a space of his own are common sources of anxiety. Likewise, poor scheduling that forces a horse to work when others are being fed or turned out not only diverts his attention but generates discontent that is sure to interfere with his performance.

## How to cure a compulsive kicker

Horses who regularly kick at their stalls, either at feeding time or in other situations that provoke anxiety, can do harm to more than the boards they encounter. A single powerful kick at just the wrong angle can produce enough force to disfigure hocks or even break bones.

Curing a compulsive kicker is difficult. The all-too-familiar method of yelling at the offender either reinforces the behavior by providing the desired attention, or completely confuses the horse because he can't make the connection between the cause (kick) and the effect (shriek). The unpleasant consequences of kicking must be consistently and immediately linked with the action itself. "Kicking chains" are commercial correctional devices available through some tack stores and catalogs. Fastened above the hock, with lengths of chain that dangle along the cannons, they deliver solid whacks on the leg with each kick. Because the kicker punishes himself, he may learn to keep his feet still even when he's anxious or anticipating.

Rearranging a kicker's environment and schedule to keep him out of compulsive mode may be more effective than trying to reform him. If he starts up when you enter the feed room to prepare the evening meal, measure his rations ahead of time and keep them in a sealed bucket by his stall. You can dump in his dinner before you begin feeding everyone else. If your horse continues to

**TERMINOLOGY**

KNOCK-KNEE

*The inward angulation of the carpus. Also known as carpus varus.*

kick while he's eating, feed him from a floor feeder in an open area where there's nothing kickable within reach. If it's turnout time that gets your compulsive type in a twitter, let him be the first one out so he won't make the noisy practice a habit.

## Kidneys: Sophisticated waste processors

Situated on either side of the spine, just beneath the last few ribs and slightly behind the area that your saddle covers, your horse's kidneys function very much like a waste-water treatment plant. Protected from impact and injury by a cushioning layer of fat, a layer of bone and several inches of muscle, the two purple organs, each weighing about a pound and a half, sort through the various substances carried in the blood, conserving those that your horse needs to survive—salt, potassium, sulfate, phosphate, glucose and amino acids—and disposing of those that could do him harm—creatinine, urea, uric acid, pigments and excess salts and water. As the kidneys carry out their basic filtration duties, they also monitor and regulate fluid volume and composition. They promote red-blood-cell production, modulate blood pressure and control the blood's pH (acidity).

Almost 99 percent of the blood filtered by the kidneys is reabsorbed, while the remaining blood constituents are excreted in the urine. Any potential waste that proves too large to fit through the kidneys' filtration tubes is rerouted to the liver or the gut wall, where it is processed for excretion with solid feces. The body's entire blood volume (on average, about 10 gallons) passes through the horse's kidneys more than 60 times in 24 hours.

## Why your horse needs vitamin K

Of the three forms of vitamin K (which is also known as menadione), those most important to your horse are present in fresh and dried green leafy plants ($K_1$) or produced in the gut by bacteria ($K_2$). Your horse uses vitamin K for blood clotting and activating a number of proteins so they can be utilized by the body.

Horses deficient in vitamin K are prone to hemorrhaging, both internally and externally. A deficiency is most likely to occur when the gut bacteria can no longer synthesize the vitamin, or the body cannot absorb or utilize it due to gastrointestinal upset—a disruption of gut flora or compromised liver function. Some anticoagulant drugs, such as warfarin, and large amounts of moldy sweet clover also interfere with vitamin K production. In these cases, injections of the synthetic version of the vitamin, $K_3$, can resolve the problem.

With regard to dietary requirements, there are no established minimums for vitamin K. It has been estimated that horses need less than 0.5 mg/kg of dry weight diet per day, an amount they can readily synthesize or derive from hay. Occasionally, foals are born with a vitamin K deficiency simply because their guts have not had time to produce it.

Dietary sources of vitamin K have very low toxicity levels, and natural poisoning has never been reported in horses. Injections of synthetic $K_3$ when the horse is not deficient can lead to renal failure, laminitis, and possibly, death within 12 hours.

## Assemble a show travel kit

The last-minute scramble to get to a horse show can dampen even the most competitive of spirits, especially when you discover that you've left something vital behind, such as your saddle, your hard hat or all of your horse's brushes.

How do you attend to all of the details and still remain focused and composed? A bit of foresight and planning go a long way toward easing that frantic feeling and making traveling with your horse a positive experience.

The following suggestions are offered as guidelines to help you develop a kit of the things you can't do without when you're on the road with your horse. As the two of you become more seasoned travelers, you'll probably add certain items and eliminate others according to your needs.

*Items for your trailer*
flashlight, two spare tires, jack, lug wrenches, head bumper for your horse
*Items for your horse's stall*
screw eyes, double-ended snaps, two water buckets, feed tub, a day's worth of bedding, wheelbarrow or muck bucket, pitchfork, rake, shovel, broom
*Items for your horse*
a day's worth of feed and hay (or as much as you can carry, to cut down on expenses at the show), medications and supplements (including salt), blanket, sheet, fishnet or wool cooler, rain sheet or canvas (depending on the weather), leg wraps, boots, hoof oil, astringents for a refreshing cooldown after a hard day's effort, grooming kit, first-aid kit
*Pieces of tack*
tack hook, saddle rack, cross ties (or a strand of baling twine for make-do cross ties), saddle, bridle, saddle pads, extra stirrup leathers, reins, girth, boots, longe line, rope shank, unbreakable halter, tack-cleaning supplies.
*Items for yourself*
show clothes, rainwear, boot polish, money, directions, maps, your veterinarian's and farrier's phone numbers, your horse's Coggin's test, your horse's health certificate (required for crossing certain state lines; check the laws of the states in which you plan to travel).

## Weak in the knees

Bad knees end the careers of both human and equine athletes. But appearances are particularly deceiving in injuries to the equine carpus, the equivalent of the human wrist. A swollen, scarred-looking joint could be sounder than one with a practically normal-looking exterior.

Highly painful, career-ending knee problems result from two processes: severe trauma and degenerative arthritis. A wrenching twist of the joint or an accidental blow can shatter bone and rip ligaments. The horse immediately is three-legged lame. This is a **Red Alert** situation. Call a veterinarian. Quick, appropriate response may save the joint, but many traumatic knee injuries deteriorate into a state of chronic, painful arthritis.

Degeneration from wear and tear sneaks up slowly, with intermittent stiff-

**VITAL STATISTICS**

KERATIN
*Horsehair is made up almost entirely of keratin, an insoluble protein containing sulfur that also makes up hoof walls and human fingernails.*

ness and an unspecified "offness" but very little outward swelling. Eventually, as the joint capsule thickens and loses some of its mobility, arthritis of the knee can put an otherwise healthy horse out of commission. Early diagnosis is important to halt the destruction.

In the ugly-but-harmless category, puffy swellings above and on the fronts of horses' knees usually are nothing more than blemishes caused by minor strains or blows. Synovial fluid has bulged around the extensor tendons, forming a "blister" that flattens under pressure but immediately refills when the pressure ceases. Neither this puffiness nor unsightly but essentially superficial scar tissue from past cuts and abrasions is likely to lead to later lameness.

A flexion test will help you decide whether your horse's knee is painful: Keep the fetlock and shoulder at normal angles to focus all pressure on the knee joint, and fold the lower leg up behind the forearm as tightly as possible. Hold the bend for approximately one minute. Release the leg, and immediately trot the horse off. If he moves with a head-bobbing limp, that knee is the probable source of pain. If he trots off no worse than before, the knee is probably not causing any gait irregularity.

## Keloid: the blemish that binds

A stiff ridge of scar tissue usually found on one of a horse's lower legs, a keloid may be more than a simple blemish. If situated near a joint, it can "bind" the horse's leg and severely handicap his athletic performance. In some cases, a bundle of nerve fibers lies trapped within, rendering the scar excruciatingly sensitive to touch or skin motion.

Keloids are preventable—but what if your horse already has one? All may not be lost.

You might be able to keep the keloid soft and pliable by working in a tenacious ointment such as zinc oxide with petrolatum or one of the many lanolin-based creams on the market. This won't banish the scar, but it may increase the joint's flexibility.

In cases where daily anointment doesn't get results or buried nerve bundles (neuromas) are part of the problem, surgery may make a dramatic difference. Some scars can be completely removed, with healthy skin moved in as replacement, while others are revised so that the shape and tension lines are less constraining, possibly restoring full function to an otherwise handicapped horse.

## A knot for his tail

Mud knots have long been a common sight at racetracks and polo fields, keeping tails high and dry even in the sloppiest footing. Even on firmer footing, a mud knot can come in handy: An upswept tail can't get tangled in the brush of overgrown trails, is safe from slips of the hand during clipping sessions and won't irritate healing hind-leg wounds.

There are innumerable techniques for fashioning a mud knot, ranging from the complex French braid favored in hunter classes to a simple knot tied at the end of the tail. But no matter what your technique, the goal is simple and unchanging: to keep your horse's tail neatly above the ground.

## And the lame hind leg is...

The telltale upward head bob when a sore front leg lands usually makes identifying front-end lameness fairly straightforward. But hind-leg lameness, especially a subtle one, can be confusing to pinpoint.

To solve the riddle, stand behind the horse and have him trotted on a loose line away from you. A horizontal reference line, such as a roofline or a fence at the height of the horse's hips, makes it easier to spot unevenness in his gait. Then have him trotted toward you, using his head as the reference point for judging his gait. Observe the entire horse, not just the suspect leg, to interpret the biomechanics of the situation:

- If one hip "hops" up higher than the other while, at the same time, the head bobs down, chances are that's the leg that hurts during weight bearing. The hop and bob reduce the amount of weight the leg has to bear.
- If both hips remain relatively level but the horse's head bobs during the forward swing of one leg, it's a sign that that leg is experiencing pain—most likely of the support structures—during the flight phase.

## Lump or bump?

Three sorts of small, firm, painless lumps commonly appear near a horse's eye:
- ***Foreign-body reactions*** (usually from a splinter or thorn tip). Tiny pene-

trating objects can get trapped in the skin. Because of the abundant circulation near the eye, they may get "sterilized" by body defenses without the usual infection and pus such items can cause elsewhere. The penetrant usually leaves a faint mark where it pierced the skin.

- *Sarcoids.* This viral tumor is slightly contagious. It often appears near the eye, perhaps inoculated by a fly into a fly bite or slight abrasion. Most are hair covered and slow growing and pose little problem for several years, at least. A few grow or multiply enough to need treatment, which may include freezing, radiation, surgery or immune stimulants, alone or in combination.
- *Melanomas.* This black-cell tumor is common near the body openings of gray horses, less so in horses of other colors. Like a sarcoid, it usually grows slowly and needs one or more treatment approaches when and if it starts enlarging significantly.

The key to small lumps is to watch them carefully, measure them with a ruler or caliper once or twice a year and record the size. Then, if you notice a growth spurt, you can get timely treatment to avoid disfigurement.

## How to make latches & locks horseproof

If your horse moonlights as an escape artist, the security of your latches and locks may be all that stands between him and disaster. Heeding a few guidelines for stall and gate closures can help keep even the most ardent escapee safely at home.

*Make it complicated.* If a latch requires a series of motions to be opened, your horse is less likely to be able to crack the code and free himself. If a 2-year-old child can figure out the mechanism, odds are good that the average horse can, too, if he tries.

*Put it out of reach.* A sliding bolt halfway down the stall door will be out of reach of curious equine lips. A second "kick bolt" at your foot level is an easy way to make any arrangement horseproof. For paddock gates, a ledge built strategically above latches will keep out prying horses, yet still allow people the access they need.

*Train yourself.* The most ingenious latches or backup bolts won't be effective if you neglect to close and fasten them. Be conscientious.

### Rely on the label

When injectable medications travel from the heated dashboard of a truck to the comfortable house and back to the frozen barn, they suffer from wide temperature fluctuations that can reduce their effectiveness or make them downright dangerous.

As a result, common equine medications carry specific storage-temperature recommendations on their labels:

- *Banamine®* is best stored between 36 and 86 degrees Fahrenheit, so the refrigerator may be the safest place for this common colic reliever.
- Injectable *phenylbutazone* is best stored between 46 and 59 degrees

Fahrenheit; if accidentally frozen, the chemical elements will crystallize.

- Storage temperatures for most *vaccines* are between 35 and 45 degrees Fahrenheit, the typical range for household refrigerators. The proteins in vaccines are particularly sensitive to temperature changes, and the critical organic matter in some can literally be "cooked" or frost-damaged by extreme climes, ruining their effectiveness and possibly making them hazardous.
- Bacteria-fighting *penicillin* requires cold storage as well (between 35 and 45 degrees Fahrenheit), but the cooled drug is quite thick and difficult to administer. Most manufacturers recommend warming the liquid between your hands after drawing it into a syringe just before injection.
- Injectable *epinephrine*, given to arrest allergic reactions, is more sensitive to light than temperature. Direct sunlight will turn the solution brown, and, if given to a horse in such a state, the drug itself can cause a reaction.

**TERMINOLOGY**

LAMINITIS

*Inflammation of the sensitive plates of soft tissue (sensitive laminae) in the horse's foot.* Acute *laminitis refers to a disturbance with rapid onset and brief duration, while* chronic *laminitis is a persistent, long-term disturbance. Either type may, in severe cases, result in founder, an internal deformity of the hoof.*

## How lame is he?

Horse owners often resort to imprecise terms—"seriously off," "kind of ouchy" or "just not right"—to describe the extent of a horse's lameness. Fortunately, the American Association of Equine Practitioners has developed a scale for grading lamenesses that gives veterinarians an objective and commonly understood language for discussing the universal equine concerns.

**Grade 1** lameness is difficult to observe and not consistently apparent under any circumstances.

**Grade 2** lameness is difficult to observe at a walk or while trotting a straight line, but it is consistently apparent under certain circumstances, such as weight carrying, circling, negotiating inclines and working on hard surfaces.

**Grade 3** lameness is consistently observable at a trot under all circumstances.

**Grade 4** lameness is obvious, with marked head nodding, hip hitching or shortened stride.

**Grade 5** lameness either causes minimal weight bearing on the affected leg while the horse is at rest and in motion, or it completely immobilizes the horse.

## When lightning strikes

You're out on a trail ride with your horse when you notice the signs of an impending thunderstorm. What's your best course of action to keep yourself and your horse out of harm's way?

Decide whether you have enough time to make it back home safely. To calculate in miles your distance from a lightning strike, count the seconds between

THE VERSATILE LIVER

*Not only does the horse's liver keep his blood clean, it also helps to keep the blood where it belongs—on the inside—by producing the agents requisite to normal blood clotting. The liver also produces an anticoagulant substance to ensure that the blood doesn't clot as long as everything is normal.*

the flash and the accompanying thunder, and divide by five. Ride away from the approaching storm, even if it means traveling in the direction opposite to home and seeking refuge at a neighboring farm.

If you are trapped outside in an electrical storm, keep a low profile. The goals are to avoid being the tallest object and to minimize your contact with the ground. Dismount and seek shelter under a thick growth of small trees, preferably on a slope but not in a puddle or creek bed. Stoop close to the ground with your feet together and head down until the storm passes. If your horse stands higher than anything else on the landscape, don't risk your own safety by holding on to him. Either tie him to a short tree to prevent him from wandering or turn him loose and allow him to rely on his own survival instincts.

## Lousy with lice

Lice are not unusual in horses, but they are rarely able to live as well on equine hosts as they do on other species. In the early spring, however, a number of factors converge to make your mount a prime target for these irritating parasites.

After a long, cold winter, horses, barns and tack are probably not at their cleanest, providing a welcoming environment for lice. And as a horse's winter coat sheds, broken hair shafts and accumulated dander offer lice their preferred food and shelter. Also, thin, aged, stressed or otherwise physically compromised horses tend to be particularly susceptible to infestation.

The two species most likely to bedevil horses are *Damalinia equi,* which feasts on its host's hair and dander, and *Haematopinas asini,* which lives on its victim's blood. They generally concentrate their activity alongside the mane, inside the thighs and around the root of the tail.

A horse infested with lice is easy to spot. The insects produce intense itchiness that often causes the host animal to gnaw at the affected areas or rub his skin raw in an attempt at relief. An adult louse is less than one-tenth of an inch long, but the movements of the little critters are faintly visible with close inspection of the skin and coat.

If you discover that your horse has lice, treat all animals, brushes, blankets and saddle pads at the barn with louse powder, which is available at your livestock or tack-supply store. For best results, thoroughly vacuum everything the next day, including the horses, to get rid of the dead and dying bugs. If you don't have a grooming vacuum, a shop or house machine will do. And while lice will quickly spread from horse to horse, take solace in the fact that equine lice cannot infect people.

## Methods for making the medicine go down

Many common equine medications are available in easy-to-administer forms. But some medications, such as oral antibiotics, come only in pill form and aren't tasty enough for a horse to eat willingly. In these cases, a bit of preparation may help the medicine to go down.

- *Break down the pills.* This can be accomplished by dissolving the medication in water or by grinding it with a mortar and pestle or a pill grinder, both of which are available at drug stores. When dissolving medication, add one more pill to the prescribed dose to allow for loss of the substance on containers and instruments, and use just enough liquid to make a runny paste.

- *Suspend the medication in something tasty.* Mix the paste or powder with something that not only tastes good but is thick enough to keep the medication from settling to the bottom. Good choices include molasses or fruit-flavored baby food. Fat-free yogurts also work well, but go for vanilla or lemon rather than flavors that contain chunky fruits. Use a very small amount to make dosing easier.

- *Load up a syringe.* Draw the mixture into a catheter-tip syringe, available from your veterinarian.

- *Down the hatch.* Standing in front and slightly to the left of your horse,

TERMINOLOGY

MOON BLINDNESS

*A recurring inflammatory disease of the eyes that sometimes leads to blindness in horses.*

grasp his halter with your left hand and slide your left thumb into the side of his mouth as if you were putting in a bit. When he opens his jaw, insert the syringe into the right side of his mouth with your right hand. Directing the tip toward the back of his tongue, deliver all the medication in one squirt. If skillfully delivered, about 70 percent of the mixture will be swallowed immediately, with the rest sticking to his tongue, to be carried down the hatch with his next swallow.

## 3 ways to minimize mud

Encrusted hides, lost shoes and slippery paddocks are cause enough to curse the mud that engulfs many parts of the country at some time each year. Here are a few things you can do to minimize the misery of mud season.

- *Fill problem areas.* If the ground around your gates and watering troughs routinely turns to muck, stabilize it before mud season with a layer of crusher-run gravel, shale or other aggregate. Raise the level of these much-trampled spots, mounding them slightly to encourage drainage away from the area.
- *Keep shoes tight.* Schedule farrier visits at shorter intervals. Delaying a reset appointment by just a few days may allow shoes to loosen enough to be sucked off by the mire. Ask your farrier about adding side clips to increase shoe security.
- *Protect your horse's legs.* A persistent crust of mud on tender equine skin encourages bacterial and fungal invaders. When your horse comes in from the mud, hose or sponge his legs with plain water and dry them thoroughly. Then slather on Desitin® or zinc oxide ointment to soothe the skin and prevent the chapping that opens the way for infectious agents.

## Clean out the medicine chest

Take a few minutes to purge your barn's medicine chest of old supplies and restock it. This simple chore could save a horse's life.

1. Check the expiration dates on prescriptions and toss outdated bottles. Old medications can be ineffective or dangerous.
2. Examine the consistency of all salves. Fluctuating temperatures cause some products to separate or harden.
3. Throw away any packages of sterile gauze or cotton wrap that have been opened and contaminated.
4. Reorder supplies in bulk with several friends to cut down on costs.

## How to make menu changes safely

Most equine caretakers know that changing feeding regimens abruptly is an open invitation to colic. But just how gradual does the transition from one feedstuff to another need to be? That depends on how dramatic a dietary shift you're making and what kind of feed is involved.

When changing concentrates, compare the labels on your old feed and new feed, and proceed as follows:

- If the total levels of digestible energy (often abbreviated as "DE") and protein are similar, your horse's gut probably won't even recognize the change. Two to three days of feeding increasingly less of the old and more of the new should allow for a trouble-free adjustment.
- If either energy or protein will increase by more than five percent, take a full week to switch over.
- With big changes, such as going from low-fat to high-fat feed or taking a leap in both energy and protein, take two weeks to complete the transition, making regular daily increments in the percentage of new feed.

Other dietary changes require equally careful introduction. A switch in roughage from poor or moderate to "rich" (from depleted pasture, for instance, to alfalfa hay) should occur over two weeks. Take three weeks to introduce emaciated animals to a high-calorie, nutrient-rich diet.

With any feeding change, be alert for signs that the gut is not adapting—diarrhea and colicky episodes are the usual indications—and revert to the previous level of nutrition or the former feedstuff until the upset passes.

## Ministering to mouth injuries

Mouth injuries are not common in horses, but when they do occur, they can make eating and drinking painful. Fortunately, oral injuries heal quickly, thanks to excellent circulation in the area.

The natural *"mouthiness"* of foals and young horses makes their age group the most vulnerable to oral wounds. Exposed bucket hangers can "fishhook" the corners of young horses' mouths, tearing their cheeks as they panic and pull away. If startled while chewing on a board or stall door, a lunging youngster can dislodge a new tooth or even break his own jaw. To prevent such injuries, cast a critical look around your young horse's living quarters, and remove all items that invite potentially hazardous snagging or chewing.

Among older horses, *improper bit fit* or use is the usual cause of mouth injuries. A bit that hangs too high or too low strikes painfully against teeth or palate; a too-small bit pinches the corners of the lips and an oversize bit doesn't distribute pressure properly. Of course, in the wrong hands, even the best-fitting bit can inflict injuries. Rub your finger along the bars, the corners of the mouth and the insides of the cheeks to test for sensitivity and cut flesh.

**AT A GLANCE**

MEASURE FOR MEASURE

*Equine nutritionists recommend feeding rations by weight instead of volume. But some caretakers stick with coffee-can measures for doling out concentrates. Weight and energy per volume vary among the feed grains, so a can's worth delivers a wide range of food value, depending on what's being served. Here's what a one-pound coffee can holds:*

- *one-half pound of wheat bran*
- *one pound of whole oats*
- *one pound of sweet feed*
- *1 1/4 pounds of pelleted concentrate*
- *1 1/2 pounds of barley*
- *1 3/4 pounds of corn.*

The only treatment for bit injuries is rest. Either suspend riding or switch to a bitless bridle (hackamore or bosal) until the area is no longer tender. Then carefully reintroduce the bridle with a different or better-adjusted bit.

Finally, *plants* can inflict oral injuries. The "fuzzy" seed heads of foxtail grass, for example, are armed with sharp, one-way barbs that won't pull out once

**VITAL STATISTICS**

OF MUSCLES & MOTION

*For all the importance put upon
them, muscles are the slaves of motion.
They cannot initiate, direct, coordinate
or modify the process. When muscles
go to work, initiation comes from nerve
impulses, direction comes from the brain.
Coordination comes from the spinal cord,
and modulation comes from sensory feed-
back to cord and brain. Nevertheless,
muscles can be trained to athletic tasks
both specific and general that make us
marvel at the versatility of the horse.*

they've penetrated flesh. When eaten by a horse, the barbs can work their way into the lining of the mouth and cause painful lesions. Afflicted horses may stop eating and drinking, and a veterinarian will have to remove the barbs.

## Health messages in manure

One of the best ways to monitor your horse's health status is to regularly examine his droppings. During your evaluation, you'll want to check out these six characteristics:

- **quantity.** The amount of manure your horse produces coincides with how well his body utilizes nutrients. If he consumes a consistent amount of feed each day and his exercise program is relatively routine, then the amount of droppings he produces will remain consistent.
- **color.** Fresh manure ranges from pale yellow to black. Its color is determined by the color of the feed the horse consumes and the amount of digestive fluid (bile) required to break it down. The more protein a feed contains, the more bile necessary for digestion. In general, protein-rich feeds cause the horse to produce darker-colored manure. A diet rich in mature grass will usually cause the horse's stool to be paler.
- **consistency.** If you can see particles of grain or blades of undigested grass in your horse's droppings, he may not be chewing his feed thoroughly. Have his teeth and mouth checked by a professional.
- **odor.** The smell of your horse's manure can signal a dietary surplus, nutritional imbalance or digestive malfunction. If his droppings smell like rotten meat, he may have too much protein in this diet, or perhaps his body is not absorbing the nutrient properly. An excess of carbohydrates in your horse's diet can cause his droppings to smell like sour biscuits.
- **moisture content.** Manure from a healthy horse is generally deposited as balls that have a slightly shiny surface. Bone-dry droppings signal dehydration. Loose stools could mean that the food your horse is eating is high in moisture and low in fiber.
- **parasites.** If you notice parasites in your horse's manure, it has been too long since he was last dewormed. You may also notice parasites a day or two after your horse has been dewormed, which is normal.

Any sudden change in the quantity or quality of your horse's manure is often an early warning that something is amiss and warrants a telephone call to your veterinarian.

## Nighttime turnout

The arrival of summer brings a flip-flop in many horse's stabling schedules—in the stall during the heat of the day, turned out during the cooler nights. Make a smooth transition to nighttime turnout by being mindful of the changes your horses will experience.

*Different insects:* Biting and blood-sucking insects, such as gnats, mosquitoes and horn flies, feast on field-kept horses during the summer, but at different times of day. Particularly sensitive horses may suffer severe allergic attacks with the onslaught of new bugs. Dawn and dusk are the periods of greatest feeding activity, so you may need to arrange your turnout schedule to be sure your horses are sheltered during these high-bug times.

*Visual adaptation:* Most horses can see well at night, but their eyes need several minutes to adjust when moving from bright light to darkness. A mass turnout from a brightly lit barn to a dark field can cause accidents as the visually impaired horses bump into each other. If you will be turning out after dark, dim the barn lights first, or stay with each horse until he appears to be negotiating the dark landscape comfortably.

*Unknown hazards:* Introducing your horse to a new environment? Turn him out before dark to give him the opportunity to explore and catalog any hazards with unrestricted vision. Along the same lines, introduce new pasturemates during daylight so they'll have made their peace before dark.

## Of all the nerve...

Among the most cost-effective tools of lameness diagnosis, nerve blocking is a systematic process of anesthetizing specific areas of the horse's body to pinpoint sources of pain. Any joint in the body, from the hoof to the hip and even in the neck, can be numbed temporarily with anesthetic. Injected along nerve pathways, the anesthetic blocks the pain receptors they serve, isolating the general location of pain but not specifying which structure—muscle, tendon, ligament, bone—is aching. Depending on the agent injected, the numbness lasts 30 minutes to three hours.

Nerve blocks are useful for determining the significance of a visible clue—a sizable splint, for instance—in a lameness. The veterinarian numbs that area only, and if the pain immediately subsides and the horse moves sound, the obvious sign is confirmed as being at least partially responsible for the problem.

When a lame horse exhibits no external clues as to the cause, the veterinarian uses a process of elimination called "bracketing" to deduce which structure is painful. If a horse is favoring one leg, for example, the nerve blocks begin with the smallest possible area—the heel's internal structures—and then, one by one, each joint up the leg is numbed. After each injection, the anesthesia is given five to 10 minutes to take effect, and then the horse is trotted off. If the lameness persists, the block is considered "negative," and the numbed area is deemed pain free. When a "positive" block numbs the nerve serving the painful area, the horse suddenly moves sound, indicating that the source of pain is within the "bracket" between the positive block and the previous negative one.

Given the key information of *where* the horse is hurting, the veterinarian can then go to work with other diagnostic tools to determine precisely what structures are involved and why they're sore.

## Investigate the source of a nosebleed

Nosebleeds are uncommon in horses (unless they happen to be racehorses, among whom "bleeding" from small lung hemorrhages is an occupational hazard). If you do discover a bloody trickle in one of your horse's nostrils and it disappears without consequence, never to appear again, the cause was probably a trifling trauma. Explore the interior of the nostril to see if you can trace the trickle back to a cut or puncture. This sort of injury to the mucosa often is inflicted by a tough hay stem or a tree branch that jabs the inside of the nostril. Blunt trauma to the head below the eyes also can cause a horse's nose to bleed. Run your fingertips over the horse's face, feeling for a spongy area and watching for pain reactions, indicating where the blow struck. Usually, head wounds below the level of the horse's eye resolve themselves without complication, so if the horse seems well in all other respects, the nosebleed requires no more attention than wiping up.

When both nostrils are producing blood or when nosebleeds are recurrent or extensive, call your veterinarian to do a diagnostic workup. Nosebleeds associated with other signs of distress, such as coughing, fever or appetite loss, are **Red Alerts** in need of immediate attention. The blood draining from distressed airways may originate in a variety of life-threatening tumors or in fungal infections of a guttural pouch in the throat.

## Do horses do more than nap?

Your horse's sleep pattern is as individual as he is—there is no standard equine "bedtime." Behavioral researchers have drawn general conclusions about equine rest, however, that may give you some clues as to why you've never caught your horse in the act.

About 20 percent of your horse's day is spent sleeping in various modes and postures. A drowsy horse catching a quick nap usually will do so standing up. An ingenious arrangement of ligaments in the front and hind legs forms the "stay apparatus" that allows a horse to remain standing with little or no muscular effort. Usually, a dozing horse will rest one hind leg and let his ears, neck and lips droop in a state of blissful relaxation. For longer naps, a horse may go into "sternal recumbency" with his legs tucked underneath him and his chin resting on the ground. This is also a favored "sunning" position in the spring. But for serious snoozing and brief periods of critical rapid-eye-movement (REM) sleep, your horse will lie flat on the ground with neck and legs outstretched. You're less likely to see him in this position for a couple of instinct-driven and physiological reasons:

- A recumbent horse in the wild is at the mercy of predators. The few seconds it takes him to rise from the ground could prove deadly. Horses in herds take turns lying down for a nap so that someone is always standing guard.
- A completely recumbent horse has compromised respiratory and circulatory functions—stresses that force him to his feet often.

As a result, a stabled horse spends an average of only five minutes at a time lying flat-out, usually in the dead of night when no one is around.

## The nictitating membranes: built in "wipers"

A horse's third eyelid normally goes unnoticed. Technically known as the nictitating membrane, this thin brown layer of tissue located just beneath the eyelid is usually no more than an unobtrusive border on the eye's inner corner. It becomes visible only when the horse yawns, tightly squeezes shut his eyes or throws up this head when he is startled.

As unassuming as it may be, however, this mucous membrane is an important part of the equine eye's protective mechanism. Similar in function to a windshield wiper, it sweeps sideways across the eyeball to clear away foreign particles, and protrudes automatically in response to certain stimuli. It owes its brown color to melanin, a pigment

**AT A GLANCE**

THE NAVICULAR BONE

*The small, boat-shaped bone that is located behind the coffin joint in the hoof, the navicular bone serves two primary functions:*

*1. It increases the size of the coffin joint, enabling the joint to absorb force and concussion.*

*2. It acts as a pulley for the deep digital flexor tendon, preventing the tendon from being torn away from the coffin bone under extreme stress.*

**VITAL STATISTICS**

NECK FACTS

*The average horse's neck accounts*
*for 25 percent of his weight and provides*
*80 percent of his balancing ability.*

that darkens it after exposure to the sun.

Although the nictitating membrane usually emerges only when a horse's eyes are closed, the next time you catch your horse peering off to one side, look closely: You'll see its thin brown edge bordering an otherwise pink membrane.

Familiarizing yourself with the third eyelid, particularly its normal texture and color, will help you spot abnormalities that accompany infection or disease. One sign of trouble, for example, is a clearly visible nictitating membrane that extends across about half of the eye. This may indicate minor irritation or local allergy. But if you detect stiffness in your horse's body and he's carrying his head at an odd angle, summon a veterinarian immediately—the protruding third eyelid may signal the onset of tetanus.

A change in the membrane's texture also is cause for concern. If its exposed edge develops a rough, cauliflower-like appearance, squamous cell carcinoma—a lumpy, irregular cancer of the superficial cells of the skin—may have taken hold. Detected early, this disorder usually can be easily treated. In many cases, it's possible to remove the affected area surgically.

## What a necropsy will tell

Though it's not pleasant to contemplate, you may one day have to decide whether to have a necropsy performed on your horse.

This postmortem examination of an animal's body (the word "autopsy" applies only to humans) is by no means required, or even useful, for every horse who dies. But your veterinarian may recommend a necropsy

- when the medical information revealed could help save other horses
- when, for insurance purposes, the exact cause of death must be determined
- when a baffling, sudden or otherwise unexpected death leaves owners and/or caretakers without answers.

In some cases, a necropsy may consist of simply gathering tissue, blood and fluid samples to be preserved and examined in a laboratory. On other occasions, the veterinarian may perform a more extensive, on-site examination of suspect areas (opening the abdomen after a colic case, for example). Very rarely, a gross necropsy, in which every system of the horse is examined, is required to establish cause of death. This usually involves transportation to a university veterinary clinic or other large pathology facility.

Whatever the extent of the investigation, a necropsy must be started soon after death to ensure that critical tissues have not yet begun to break down. That's why, as painful as it may be, the time to discuss the advisability of a necropsy with your veterinarian is *before* your horse dies or is put down.

## When is a horse overtired?

While exertion and some degree of metabolic and physical stress are necessary to achieve any increase in fitness, too much at one time can make a horse more susceptible to illness, injury, even colic and kidney failure. Because fatigue can reach many different levels, no one sign indicates an overtaxed system. But warning signs include:

- patchy sweating, especially on a cold, clammy horse
- disinterest in food and surroundings
- clumsy movement.

Perhaps the best determinant of exhaustion is the heart-rate recovery index, a measure of how rapidly a horse recuperates from stressful work. If you suspect your horse has overexerted himself, keep him still for about five minutes, then take his pulse by feeling the artery that crosses the lower jawbone or listening with a stethoscope just above the left elbow. Typically, but not always, fit horses have a heart rate of 64 beats per minute or less after a five-minute rest period. Fatigued horses, on the other hand, usually will have a heart rate of 70 beats or more per minute. After counting the number of heartbeats for one minute, jog the horse about 125 feet and stop. Wait another 30 seconds or so, then take his pulse again. Ideally, the second reading will be lower than the first. If it is 10 percent or more higher, the horse has been worked beyond his fitness level.

Most pleasure mounts never reach such a level of fatigue. But a horse who is idle all week and then taken out for an all-day ride may suffer mild symptoms of overexertion, calling for a better conditioning program or a more sensible work schedule.

## What are osselets?

Unique to racehorses, osselets are the fibrous and/or bony lumps that form on the front of the fetlock joint. During high-speed gallops, the fetlock joints of speed horses, particularly those with long pasterns, can extend (dorsiflex) so much that the pasterns sink almost parallel with the track surface. A callus of sorts forms on the joint's front face where the top of the long pastern bone hammers against the lower end of the cannon bone. In the initial stages of osselet formation, the area is very sore, but once the horse is taken out of speed work, the pain subsides and only the painless bony callus remains.

## Oat notes

Though modern feeding practices rely more on sweet feeds and pelleted mixes than plain cereal grains, oats are still considered the standard horse feed and probably always will be.

Oats are the seeds of mature oat grass. They can be fed unprocessed as harvested, or "rolled" to crack the tough outer shell, which is difficult for some horses to digest. So-called "racehorse oats" are steamed and rolled to remove dust and increase digestibility. "Naked" oats, a genetically selected form, have loose hulls that fall away when the grain is harvested, producing a more digestible, energy-packed, lower-fiber concentrate.

Contrary to the old saw about "feeling his oats," a horse is not likely to become unmanageable or overly energetic after eating oats. In fact, pound for pound, oats are lower in energy than corn or barley, making them a relatively inefficient, expensive feed. At the same time, oats are the safest feed grain for horses, since they are not subject to the molds and mycotoxins that can grow on corn and other high-energy feeds. Additionally, their low starch and high fiber content make them unlikely to induce laminitis and colic. A horse has to consume about double the weight of oats compared to other grains to get the carbohydrate overload that triggers these dire physical conditions.

Finally, most horses relish the nutty flavor of oats, so they're a good bet for finicky eaters. Their high fiber content also increases the heat of the digestive process, making oats a useful dietary choice in very cold climates where forage alone can't supply enough calories.

**AT A GLANCE**

CARE FOR OLDER HORSES

**Vaccinations:** *Older horses are more susceptible to infections. Protect them from encephalitis, tetanus, rhinopneumonitis and influenza with regular vaccinations.*

**Deworming:** *Older horses acquire parasites more easily and may experience more damage or debility from the common types of worms. An effective deworming program will protect normal gut function.*

**Trimming and shoeing:** *Ease the unavoidable arthritic changes of age and alleviate additional stress to the legs by "going with" older horse's natural hoof-growth tendencies when you trim and shoe.*

## A poultice primer

Poulticing is an ancient and versatile treatment method. Designed to relax tissues and draw out swelling, infection and local soreness, a poultice is any hot or cold substance that holds moisture next to the skin.

Modern-day poultices usually combine traditional mediums, such as fine clay or special mud, with antiphlogistics, substances that draw fluids to the surface and act as mild counterirritants to increase circulation. Essential oils, such as eucalyptus, camphor and mint, are the antiphlogistics in many modern preparations, and ichthammol, a gooey, tarlike substance, remains unrivaled in its drawing, antiseptic and soothing properties.

The temperature and drawing properties of poultices, along with the support of a bandage, work to soothe a number of injuries and stress points:

- Cooling earth poultices, such as kaolin or Denver mud, benefit *strains* and *sprains*. Apply the poultice to the affected area and, to reduce later laundry work, cover with plastic wrap before bandaging. Change the poultice each day. Many become ineffective upon drying. Read the label carefully, however. Some earth poultices are designed to dry as they work.
- Packing the sole of the foot with ichthammol or various muds encourages *hoof abscesses* to drain. Bran is also convenient for hoof poultices and can be mixed with Epsom salts for "drawing" action, or Listerine®, which

adds a counterirritant property.

- "Spot" poultices, ichthammol or other adherents dabbed onto swellings to help draw out heat and inflammation, reduce *insect stings* and *random lumps* and *bumps*.
- Preventive poultices ease *tired legs*, lessening the likelihood of *swelling* and *strains*. But remember that wrapping over a counterirritant, such as Absorbine®, can blister tender or injured skin.
- *Open wounds* are best poulticed only under the guidance of your veterinarian, because deep puncture wounds and injuries near joints can become worse if treated incorrectly.

## Poisonous-plant protection

Provided that they have an adequate nutritious diet containing ample fiber, most horses are unlikely to eat poisonous plants that may somehow find their way into your pasture. In general, horses possess a refined palate by the time they reach maturity, and, fortunately, the taste, texture and/or smell of toxic plants are offensive to them.

Nonetheless, extreme hunger, curiosity or boredom can cause a horse to eat plants or tree parts that sicken or kill him. To protect your horse form this possibility:

- Provide adequate pasture and grain.
- Inspect the contents of hay and bedding.
- Keep cuttings, prunings and discarded garden plants out of your pasture and away from your horses.
- After storms or periods of high winds, promptly check pastures for broken tree limbs, especially those with wilting leaves.
- Keep horses away from ornamental shrubbery, plants and flowers.
- Learn to recognize the poisonous plants in your area and familiarize yourself with the signs of poisoning—for instance, a digestive upset or a drastic change in your horse's behavior.
- If you suspect that your horse has eaten something poisonous, call your veterinarian immediately and supply him with as much information as possible. The more details you can provide, the better the practitioner's chances of helping your horse recover.

## Can a pony carry a full-grown rider?

Ponies generally are quite strong for their size, and speed is more injurious to them than the amount of weight they are carrying. Beyond those generalizations, it's best to analyze each large rider/small horse decision on its own merits. Consider, for example, that Island or Scottish Shetlands are tiny draft horses that are very strong. American Shetlands have been refined for fine-harness competition and are relatively frail. In contrast, Arabian horses tend to be sturdy for their size—14-hand endurance horses have carried 200 pounds quite successfully at slower speeds.

The matter of balance—the "fit" of the rider to the horse—is also important. Horses and people each maintain natural rhythms when they are in motion, and very tall people often have difficulty balancing on small horses, irrespective of weight factors. Imbalance leads to stumbling, staggering, risk and injury.

## Ways to prevent proud flesh

Any time your horse has a gaping cut, there is a chance that proud flesh could develop. An abnormal, fragile, pink to reddish-colored mass of tissue growing out of the wound, proud flesh results when normal healing goes awry.

Several factors encourage proud flesh:

- *the size of the wound.* A cut that is very wide and has not been sutured will be more prone to develop proud flesh than a smaller injury, such as a puncture, simply because there is more area for skin cells to cover.
- *the location of the wound.* Cuts on a horse's lower legs tend to be more prone to proud flesh because the blood pressure in that area is relatively high. As a result, it promotes the production of granulation tissue within and above the wound base.
- *inflammatory agents.* Irritants, such as dirt, bacteria, cloth fibers, harsh soaps and antiseptics, can cause tissues to become inflamed, creating more circulation in the wound and stimulating excess granulation as a result.
- *any trauma that slows the healing process on the surface,* making it easier for granulation to get out of control. Biting, scratching or motion, for instance, can disrupt healing.

The best way to prevent a cut from turning into an angry mass of proud flesh is to keep a close eye on the healing process. Whenever your horse comes in from the field with a cut, clean the wound thoroughly and keep it clear of dirt and debris. Use a very mild surgical soap only for the initial cleanup, rinsing well. Then apply anti-bacterial wound medication and a nonstick sterile bandage. These will be the least irritating to sensitive healing skin. If you use a supportive dressing, wrap it with moderate and even pressure. Too much pressure can potentially destroy injured skin and/or encourage proud flesh.

**VITAL STATISTICS**

PERIPHERAL PULSE

*There are four prime locations on the horse's body where his peripheral pulse can be felt and recorded:*

*1. on the outside of the hind leg below the hock*

*2. on the foreleg over the sesamoid bones*

*3. two places on the lower jaw*

*4. in the central artery of the ear.*

## How to pull a shoe

No matter how reliable your farrier is, it's not always possible for him to be there when you need him. Since horses seem to have a knack for partially pulling off shoes, twisting them or springing one branch at an inopportune time, learning to remove a shoe can help you safeguard your horse's soundness if an emergency develops.

To pull a shoe, you'll need a clinch cutter and hammer (or a farrier's rasp) and a shoe puller. You'll start by removing any remaining nail clinches—the protruding nail points that have been bent to lie flat against the hoof's outer wall. After cleaning your horse's foot with a hoof pick, turn to face the same direction as he is. Move his foot forward until his leg is extended and, as you squat slightly, rest his foot just above your knee. If you have a clinch cutter and hammer, place the edge of the cutter directly under the nail tip and use the hammer to strike upward. Taking care not to gouge the hoof surface, repeat the process to remove all the clinches.

If you're using a rasp, place the fine-cut surface parallel to the ground and sweep it sharply across a clinch to rasp it off. With this method, be careful not to bang the horse's coronary band.

Once all of the clinches are gone, use the shoe puller to remove the shoe. Pivot to face your horse's hindquarters and place his foot on your knees. Being careful not to nip any of the hoof, close the pincers of the shoe puller at one heel between the wall and the shoe. Lift the shoe away from the heel and toward the toe, raising it 1/4 to 1/2 inch off the hoof. Knock the shoe back down so that the nail heads are prominent. Pull the nails one at a time. Repeat the same process with the other heel and continue, alternating sides until the last nail is pulled, allowing the shoe to fall off. Once off, the shoe should be thrown clear so your horse doesn't step on it.

## Pinkeye problems

When your horse has a swollen eye, it's always cause for concern, but it may just be conjunctivitis, or pinkeye, an easily treated bacterial infection. Afflicted eyes often swell completely shut, with the bright pink conjunctiva (the mucous membranes that line the eyelids) appearing to ooze out between the lids.

Remembering that your horse is likely to be touchy about having his eye examined, use the thumb and forefinger of one hand to gently spread the lids apart and inspect the eyeball itself for signs of trouble. A bright, healthy globe indicates that the problem is in the lids alone. Any abnormalities of the eyeball constitute a **Red Alert** situation. Call your veterinarian immediately.

Equine conjunctivitis is caused when trauma to the tissues surrounding the eye opens the way for bacterial invasion. For instance, when face flies are attracted to the moisture around a horse's eye, the horse rubs the area on his knee to rid himself of the irritation. The insects depart, but any bacteria they were carrying remain to be rubbed into the eyelid's sensitive membranes. Windblown dust also leads to eye irritation, rubbing and subsequent infection. Unlike pinkeye in cattle, equine conjunctivitis is not an airborne contagion, but horses can contract particularly virulent strains from each other through direct contact.

Treatment for conjunctivitis is topical antibiotic eye ointment, which you can get from your veterinarian. If your horse has recurring eye infections, you may want to keep ointment on hand for use at the first signs of irritation. With treatment and removal of the irritant, the swelling of conjunctivitis should subside in about two days. In insect season, equip your horse with a fly mask and keep him sheltered during daylight hours, when face flies are active.

## What's your pasture's health status?

You don't need a PhD in animal science or agronomy to evaluate pasture quality. Suspect that your pasture's health isn't up to par if you notice:
  • *muddy or downtrodden patches.* Often located in the vicinity of feeders, salt

blocks and waterers, such damage results when first the grass and then the topsoil can no longer stand up to the constant abuse of equine hooves.

- *nearly bare or closely cropped patches.* The succulent new growth may provide horses with a tasty meal, but without a chance to mature, the blades lose their ability to hold their ground, and eventually the pasture's yield is reduced.
- *tall, rangy stalks.* Even hungry horses can be picky eaters, and they may undergraze certain areas of the pasture. The longer the grass grows, the less nutritious it becomes. It also may create shade that stunts the growth of younger plants.
- *weeds.* In high percentage these pasture invaders not only rob the more palatable plants of moisture and nutrients, they deprive the horses of a portion of their daily ration as well.

Even more important than your visual inspection, however, is a soil test to detect the chemical composition of the ground that's supporting your horses' daily fare. Agents from agricultural as well as from county and cooperative extension services, or representatives of commercial testing firms can help you with this evaluation, which is most beneficial for comparative purposes when it's performed on an annual basis. By analyzing samples of the top four inches of soil at various locations in your pasture, the consultant will be able to tell you which nutrients are present in abundance and which are lacking in the makeup of your soil. He'll also recommend the techniques that will be most effective in maintaining or restoring the area where your horses graze.

**AT A GLANCE**

PHOSPHORUS FACTS

- *Hay and cereal grains contain the mineral phosphorus, but the form found in hay is much more readily utilized by the horse.*
- *A 1,100-pound horse in light work requires 14 grams of phosphorus daily, an amount that can be supplied by 9 pounds of oats or barley or 15 pounds of timothy hay.*
- *Horses on pasture year-round can store phosphorus in the spring and early fall to make up for deficient supplies in the summer and winter.*

## Pinpoint the source of pain

Certain signs of pain clearly point to the source of a horse's discomfort. Of course, some disorders, like colic and founder, can have multiple effects that are manifested throughout the animal's body. And a single sign of distress can point out more than one specific problem. The key is to be aware of the basic signs of pain, explore their ramifications and consult a veterinarian whenever you suspect that trouble is brewing.

Common signs of pain and their probable sources include:

- *limping*—leg pain from various sources
- *pointing a toe*—soreness from an abscess, navicular disease or shoulder injuries
- *walking "wide" or holding a knee to the side*—joint pain
- *standing with a dropped hip or shoulder*—nerve damage or dislocation
- *hiking a hip during movement*—hind-leg lameness
- *short, "stabby" strides, choppy movement*—foot pain, navicular disease, shoulder pain or back pain
- *shifting weight from side to side*—navicular disease or joint pain

65

- *peculiar stance*—sawhorse stance (splay-footed) or camped out (hind legs extended behind) could mean colic; hind legs brought forward underneath the body may indicate laminitis
- *pinned ears, raised head during grooming or saddling*—muscle or skin pain
- *chewing strangely*—tooth trouble, yellow star thistle poisoning
- *grinding teeth*—ulcers, gastrointestinal tract pain or any severe pain
- *kicking during specific movement* (transitions, backing up, etc.)—stifle pain or back pain
- *dullness, lack of appetite*—internal pain
- *stiffness of neck*—muscular pain from strain, injection-related abscesses
- *pawing*—internal pain or anxiety
- *rolling*—internal pain or skin reactions
- *lying down*—internal pain or foot soreness
- *biting at sides, looking around at body*—internal pain
- *stretching out neck*—sore throat
- *increased pulse, respiration*—internal pain, stress or exertion, or, if accompanied by increased digital pulse, leg pain.

## A perspective on puncture wounds

Loosely defined as any cut that is deeper than it is wide, a puncture wound offers anaerobic bacteria a free ride deep into your horse's body tissues. Unlike other wounds, puncture wounds don't drain well, which allows those bacteria to flourish in an airless environment. And the area closest to the skin seals and heals first, trapping the bacteria and often causing abscesses or deep-seated infections. To make matters worse, part of the puncturing item can break off deep in the wound, thwarting the healing and rehabilitation processes.

Not all puncture wounds are life threatening, of course, but it takes a veterinarian's trained eye to distinguish critical puncture wounds from benign ones. For this reason, treat *any* puncture wound as a potential **Red Alert** situation and immediately summon a veterinarian to examine and treat your horse.

## The purpose of pus

Pus is the product of the body's self-cleaning mechanism for wounds. Good pus is sterile, and bad pus is infected. Pus of either sort finds its way out by escalating pressure until the skin surface erupts. Through this action, the cavity is cleared of contamination and debris, and the pus itself blocks new contaminants that would enter the wound while it supports newly forming vessels being generated to fill the gap in the flesh.

Good pus is smooth, creamy and of a pinkish-tan color that dries to the healthy reddish brown of a scab. It has no odor beyond a faint fleshy aroma. In contrast, bad pus is thinner or of inconsistent texture, containing particles or lumps. Bad pus is darker, even gray, black or greenish. It often smells bad. Wounds exuding good pus get less and less swollen, painful and disabling, whereas bad pus persists or increases in volume.

With appropriate antibiotics, surgery, dressing techniques and nursing care, bad pus can be converted to good pus in most cases. Your veterinarian will provide you with the appropriate treatment strategy for the conversion.

## Rx for a quarter crack

It's possible for a horse to injure a coronary band and initiate a quarter crack, a vertical crack in the part of the hoof wall between the heel and toe. An ordinary quarter crack that does not involve inflammation or weeping should not require months of inactivity to grow out normally. When the coronary band is bruised, the injury mechani-

cally separates that area of the wall from the sensitive germinal corium above. The injured corium may produce little new horn for a day or two, then a rush of new horn may slightly bulge above the "old" horn. This horizontal defect can be a "stress riser" from which a vertical crack propagates if the foot is not trimmed to support it evenly.

If a properly stabilized vertical crack doesn't bleed or lengthen upward and the horse isn't limping, you can ride your horse moderately (two to three times per week in the ring, on the trail or cross-country) during the "growing out" period. If a triangle of wall breaks out along the rear of the crack, repair material and a side clip can keep things under control while you use the horse. Turning the horse out in bell boots to prevent injury is common and usually safe. A horse who repeatedly "grabs" himself may be trimmed or shod so as to discourage this.

## 7 steps for quarantine

To prevent the spread of disease from resident horses who become ill or new arrivals of unknown health status, horse facilities large and small need a quarantine management policy and a physical setting for isolating horses. The following steps can keep contagion from spreading through the air or via carriers (tack, insects, equipment, water and caretakers) to the rest of the herd:

1. Set up your quarantine area far enough away to protect healthy horses. Allow at least 300 feet of separation if the uninfected group is downwind of the quarantine area, and 20 feet if the uninfected horses are upwind from the quarantine area. (If your property doesn't allow for such distances, you can create an isolation stall by extending the walls to the ceiling with plastic sheeting or plywood. This will block airflow to the rest of the building, but you will probably need to install fans to provide circulation within the enclosure.)

2. Be sure quarantine fields do not share fence lines with "clean" fields. Wait several days after quarantined horses leave the field before you restock it with healthy horses.

3. Water quarantined horses from their own separate sources. Some infectious agents can survive for several days in water and on watering equipment.

4. Use a separate set of maintenance tools for the quarantine area. Pitchforks, wheelbarrows and even brooms offer pathogens a free ride to other areas of the farm.

5. Care for quarantined animals after tending to the healthy horses. Because disease agents can cling to your clothing and hair, make feeding, medicating and cleaning up after the isolated horses your final chores of the caretaking cycle. If it's not possible to leave them until last, shower and change clothing (including shoes or boots) before tending to the rest of the herd.

6. Minimize traffic in quarantine areas. Visitors, vehicles and even pets can transport contagion. Post signs to warn visitors away from the quarantine area, and, if necessary, confine dogs, barn cats and other stable denizens to control their contact with quarantined animals.

7. Disinfect quarantine stalls and tools after the occupant departs. Use a mild bleach solution to scrub stall-cleaning equipment, feed and water buckets, stall mats, grooming tools and other portable items that came in contact with the horse or his wastes, and let everything dry in the sun. Use the same solution to scrub down wood or cinder-block stall walls, or rent a power washer.

## Why do horses roll?

An experienced eye can easily spot a horse preparing to roll. The pacing in circles, blowing of dirt and slightly bent knees all signal the impending maneuver. While the preparations are nearly universal, where, when and why horses roll is as individual as the animals themselves. In general, a horse drops for one of three reasons:

- *pleasure*—for the sheer fun of it
- *practical*—self-maintenance or grooming
- *pathological*—to relieve pain or discomfort.

A horse who drops quietly to the ground soon after being untacked probably is just enjoying himself. He may be easing the irritation of drying sweat, or, if he was hosed off after a ride, he could be drying himself with dirt and, at the same time, gaining a layer of protection from insects.

Whatever the reason, the selection of the proper site is an integral part of the rolling process. A horse often will find a favorite spot in his paddock and return there every time. When a horse drops his head and "blows" at the ground, he's checking to make sure that it is indeed his spot, it still has an adequate amount of dirt and it's still free of debris that could interfere with a good roll.

Often a number of horses in a field share a prime rolling location and will take turns wallowing in its pleasures.

## Reading rings & ridges on hooves

Patterns of hoof growth provide a constantly updated catalog of injury, illness and nutritional status for the whole horse as well as the local area. Inflammation is the impetus for most hoof irregularities: An inflamed coronary band produces thicker—but not healthier—horn, resulting in rings, ridges and bumps on the hoof surface. A starved coronary band, in contrast, produces less or thinner horn, which appears as a groove. You can study the hooves' "landscape" to gather insights into your horse's medical history.

- A single ring on all four hooves is a common aftereffect of serious, acute illness. Bodywide illness suppresses horn growth for a short time, producing a distinct ring around the entire hoof. A serious respiratory infection, for example, can leave hoof rings that remain visible long after the horse recovers.
- Multiple, evenly spaced rings and ridges are the marks of repeated cycles of inflammation and recovery that have made the horse's hooves weak and brittle.
- Multiple rings farther apart at the heel than at the toe indicate chronic laminitis. Lack of circulation in the toe area also may cause a distinctive "swale," or dish, there.
- A single rogue bump on a hoof is likely the result of local trauma, such as an abscess or injury to the coronary band. Inflammation in one spot on the coronet produces a solitary bulge that migrates toward the ground as the hoof grows, sometimes weakening the wall and leading to an associated hoof crack.

Horn growth usually returns to normal when inflammation subsides. As the coronary band generates new hoof wall, defects move down the hoof until they are trimmed or worn away, a process that takes nearly a year for most horses.

## How to get rid of ringworm

When is a worm not a worm? When it's ringworm—a highly transmissible fungal infestation of the skin that requires quick, conscientious action if it is to be banished from your farm.

Despite the "ring" in its name, the fungal infection produces noncircular, feathery flaking of the skin, thick "orange peel" patches, or large, distinct scabs covering creamy pus. Unlike the somewhat similar rainrot, ringworm lesions are painless and covered in scurf or loose scabs.

Ringworm is transmissible from horse to horse via tack, blankets, brushes, even stall walls and a favorite scratching post. Interspecies infection—among you, your dogs, your cattle or most any other critter on the infected premises—is common. If you discover ringworm on one horse, chances are the rest of your herd has been exposed. Infections covering extensive areas of your horse's hide need a veterinarian's attention, but you may be able to control a minor outbreak on your own.

To stop ringworm's spread, wear rubber gloves and bathe the infected horse with a human dandruff shampoo. Work off the scabs and crusts, and rub undiluted shampoo directly into the bare patch. Rinse after five minutes. If you have the time and resources, wash the horses who aren't showing signs, too, and rinse them lightly to leave just a bit of residue from the shampoo as a preventive measure.

Next, attack your tack. Use a 50-50 solution of Mr. Clean and Lexol to wash every piece of leather that may have come in contact with the affected horse. The disinfectant kills the fungus, while the oil protects the leather. Blankets, saddle pads, bandages, brushes and other washable items should be soaked in a strong solution of chlorine bleach and water, and then triple rinsed.

After you've done all that, you may want to use a mixture of bleach and water to disinfect your wash stall, cross-ties and fences in communal areas. And don't shift stall or pasture assignments until the fungus has been defeated. You'll know ringworm is gone when no new lesions have shown up in the herd and hair starts to regrow in the treated patches.

## Recovering from respiratory infection

Signs of a respiratory infection can range in severity from a mild cough to drippy nostrils, lethargy and labored breathing. But, regardless of the extent of the illness, attentive nursing helps to speed recovery and prevent relapses.

If your horse shows signs of an infection, he probably already has spread the disease to his herdmates, so don't waste your energy on quarantines. Instead, designate an easily accessible sick-bay stall that is well-ventilated but draft-free. Deep, dust-free bedding is a must, especially if your horse spends most of his recuperative time lying down. Clean the stall at least twice a day.

A stall-bound horse requires much less energy than an active one, so cut back on grain. Remember, however, that the healing process does require some energy. If your patient begins shivering or losing weight, raise his ration again. Inspect hay meticulously for signs of mold or dust, and dampen it before giving it to your horse. Replace automatic waterers with buckets to monitor intake, and resist the urge to add anything to "tempt" the horse to drink—cool, clean water is always the best option.

All but the most desperately sick horses can be hand-walked and hand-grazed. A short stroll twice a day helps improve respiration, digestion and circulation while lifting an ill horse's spirits. Grazing also gives gravity a chance to clear out respiratory secretions. But be very cautious when timing your horse's return to work: Respiratory tissues take an average of three weeks to heal, so a good convalescence guideline for a minor infection is three days off for every day the horse showed signs of illness. When you do return him to work, do so gradually. Too much too soon can set a recovering horse into a relapse or cause scarring of the lungs and long-term problems.

## It's rainrot

The signs are unmistakable: A few hours after coming in from the rain, your horse's coat begins to stand up in a peculiar pattern, either bordered by the "drip line" of rain runoff or in patches. As you smooth it down, you feel a radiating heat, and your horse flinches from your touch. By the next day, sensitive, tight scabs have appeared where the rain was concentrated, making your horse a miserable mess. The culprit? Rainrot.

Rainrot is caused by *Dermatophilus spp.,* bacteria that normally live without consequence in the equine coat. However, a rain followed by slow-drying, humid conditions enables the organism to multiply, which irritates the hair follicles and skin of afflicted horses. The scabbing, which may range in severity from a light "peppering" to a continuous, painful sheet, follows the runoff pattern of water over the horse's back and rump. Rarely do subsequent rains initiate new areas of infection.

The earlier you detect rainrot, the easier it will be to spare your horse the discomfort and cosmetic problems associated with it. A brief course of penicillin injections started at the initial signs of a raised coat will solve the problem without hair loss. If you begin penicillin after the scabs appear, the treatment will still be effective, but healing will take longer. Without treatment, rainrot runs its course in one to four weeks, depending on the extent and severity of the scabbing. As healing progresses, resist the urge to pick the scabs, as they are very painful and can bleed. Instead, soften them with mineral oil and let them work themselves loose. Then apply a mild, medicated shampoo and try to gently rub the scabs free with your fingertips. If the scabs don't slip off easily, oil them again.

Preventing rainrot is a matter of good grooming. A dirty coat naturally contains more organisms and more skin debris to feed them. Twice-weekly or more frequent brushing or vacuuming usually limits the incidence and severity of rainrot. Some horses, however, are particularly susceptible and may need to be protected from wet weather to prevent future attacks. To guard against the spread of rainrot, it's wise not to share brushes, tack and blankets belonging to afflicted horses.

## AT A GLANCE

### RINGBONE: HIGH & LOW

*Ringbone is the formation of new bone around joints below the fetlock. The condition usually evolves slowly over years of heavy work on concussive footing. Lameness usually comes on slowly, marked by a gait in which the heel strikes the ground first.*

**High ringbone** *occurs at the joint linking the long and short pastern bones. Even when this joint loses all flexibility by fusing completely, the horse can be pain-free and sound.*

**Low ringbone** *forms inside the hoof in the joint connecting the short pastern and coffin bones. This joint must have full mobility for proper foot function, so an afflicted horse may never be serviceably sound again.*

## The right time for new shoes

Let your horse, rather than the calendar, be your primary guide when you're considering when to replace his shoes. The right time to reshoe is a function of individual hoof condition and a horse's activity level. Horses subjected to a demanding performance schedule, as well as those with weak or injured feet, require frequent reshoeing—perhaps as often as every three to four weeks. In contrast, horses with strong, healthy hooves who receive only light use may require a farrier's attention as little as every 10 weeks.

To determine the best shoeing schedule for your horse, start by studying his shoes. It's time to call the farrier if a shoe is bent or shows signs of uneven wear, if it has lost half of its original thickness, or if its nail heads are worn down to nearly nothing.

Next examine the hooves for
- cracking in, around or between nail holes
- flaring (bending outward and upward) of the foot's bottom edge on the iron
- protruding "clinches"—nail ends that were bent flat against the outside of the hoof at the time of shoeing but that now extend away from the hoof wall
- excessive space (a quarter inch or more) between the shoe and the edge of

the sole—noticeable when cleaning the foot with a hoof pick

• areas of overgrowth where the hoof wall extends beyond the shoe's edge.

Waiting too long to have your horse reshod can have serious effects on his performance and soundness. Old shoes may begin to press on the sole and damage it, straining the joints of the foot and precipitating hoof-wall breakage. In addition, they're likely to become loose and fall off. By recognizing the signs of worn-out shoes, you can help prevent hoof problems and shoe no less—or more—often than necessary.

## Why saline's the best solution

Physiologic saline solution (PSS, or just plain "saline") is the least complex item in your first-aid kit, but it may be the most important one. This salt-and-water mixture, balanced to be compatible with internal tissues, is perfect for flushing wounds and cleansing eyes. Plain water is harsher than saline, and actually ruptures and kills additional cells. Saline solution rinses wounds clean with little cell damage, promoting quicker, less complicated healing.

The most convenient form of saline to keep in your first-aid kit is a squirt bottle of contact-lens solution. Make sure it contains 0.9 percent salt—stronger or weaker solutions won't have the same benefits. For greater quantities, you can prepare a homemade saline solution by mixing one tablespoon of salt in a gallon of warm water. Fill a catheter-tip syringe or a Water-Pik from this larger supply to flush an extensive wound clear of debris and loose fragments of tissue.

## To protect against sunburn

Overexposure to the sun's ultraviolet rays has left your horse with painful, peeling blisters on his white markings. To ease the pain of sunburn, apply a soothing skin cream. To prevent the problem from recurring, cover your horse's white markings with zinc oxide, sunscreen or gentian violet before you turn him out, or keep him indoors during the day.

## Should you pick that scab?

A scab is a dried collection of white blood cells and other body fluids that have diffused into a wound to stem the flow of blood, combat infection and provide a natural dressing. Ideally, an injury will have been cleaned and treated before a scab forms. Then the scab should be left alone to seal the wound and protect against contamination. If, however, a scab has formed over an uncleaned wound, bacteria and other contaminants are likely to have been sealed within an environment favorable for their growth. This is a common problem with puncture wounds. In these cases, the scab must be removed to expose the wound for a thorough cleaning. Soaking with warm-water compresses will soften the scab, making it easier to remove.

The tight, clinging scabs of rainrot and scratches result from skin infections. External treatments call for exposing the responsible bacteria, but picking off the scabs can be painful for your horse and unhygienic for other animals that you may touch. Instead, smear ichthammol over the affected areas (covering with plastic wrap, if possible) and wait until the scabs loosen and slide off with only gentle encouragement.

## How to tell when a horse has eaten too much sand

Sand accumulation in a horse's gut can lead to serious colic. Fortunately, you can identify and control the problem before colic occurs. Here's how to run a fecal test for the presence of intestinal sand deposits:

1. Fill a two-quart plastic container about two-thirds full of water, and mark the water level on the outside of the container.
2. Add six large manure balls from your horse. Mark the new water level on the container. These marks will allow you to repeat the test using exactly the same amounts of water and manure for continued monitoring.
3. Mix the manure and water into a slurry, then allow it to stand for an hour or more so the heavier sand will settle to the bottom of the container.
4. Carefully pour off the slurry and measure the sand left behind.

If one-quarter teaspoon or more of sand remains, the horse is ingesting significant amounts. To clean up his eating habits, avoid feeding hay directly off the ground. A large carpet remnant or rubber mat may prevent horses fed outdoors from consuming grit along with their hay. Good pasture management will keep plants at sufficient grazing height so that bare earth is not exposed. A daily dose of psyllium—a mildly laxative seed that expands and turns gelatinous in contact with moisture in the gut—may help move some sand out of the intestines, but its efficacy is still under review.

## 6 steps to a drier stall

A wet stall is smelly, unsightly and detrimental to a horse's hooves and respiratory health. By incorporating the following steps into your daily stall-cleaning routine, you can ensure that your horse's habitat remains fresh and inviting.

**ALL'S WELL**

SKIN-PINCH TEST

*Time test used to determine a horse's hydration level. The longer it takes for a fold of skin on the horse's neck to return to normal, the more dehydrated he is. One to two seconds signifies adequate hydration; six to 10 seconds represents severe dehydration.*

**Step 1:** *Seek out wet spots.* After picking up all the manure in the stall, systematically turn over the bedding, looking for wet spots. The intense smell of ammonia will tip you off to the presence of urine, and both straw and shavings will appear darker.

**Step 2:** *Dig them up.* Remove all wet bedding, down to the floor. If you have earthen floors, rake the damp spot to ensure that all the bedding is taken up. A good-quality spring-tooth rake is best for the job. Stalls that have been cleaned haphazardly before may have a smelly layer of muck to remove. Keep raking and digging until you see the floor.

**Step 3:** *Air out the stall thoroughly.* Toss the clean bedding against the walls, and leave the wet spots exposed for as long you can (time your stall cleaning with the start of turnout). Leave barn windows and doors open to encourage drying breezes.

**Step 4:** *Lime the spots well.* A layer of hydrated (slack) or agricultural lime absorbs moisture, neutralizes ammonia and inhibits bacterial growth. (Do not use dehydrated lime, also called "quick" lime, "hot" lime or mason's lime, which is extremely caustic.) Hydrated lime easily forms dust clouds that, if inhaled, can severely irritate human airways. Agricultural lime is less irritating but not as absorbent.

**Step 5:** *Use bedding strategically.* When the stall has dried, rake the smaller bits of bedding into the limed areas first. These powdery particles are more absorbent than larger pieces of bedding and will soak up any remaining moisture as well as subsequent additions. Pull the clean bedding from the walls, spread it throughout the stall and add new bedding as needed. Bed the habitual urination areas only as deeply as necessary to soak up the moisture, leaving less to remove the next time.

**Step 6:** *Housebreak the occupant.* Consider teaching your horse to urinate outside his stall, especially if he has continual access to an adjoining paddock or pen.

## RED ALERT

SHOCK

*Failure of the vital body systems, characterized by loss of blood volume and pressure, shallow breathing and rapid heartbeat. Usually the direct and potentially fatal by-product of extremely serious injury, stress or illness.*

## Health messages in sweat

The lather on your horse's coat after a hard trail ride is meant to cool him, but it's also a useful indicator of his health and fitness. Sweat appears first where the skin is thinnest and most mobile: on the ears, flanks, elbows, chest and inner thighs. Next to lather up are the areas covered by tack, followed by the neck and face. When the backs of the rump and thighs begin to bead up with perspiration, you can be sure the heat or workload is seriously stressing your horse.

At the start of warm weather, a horse's sweat is likely to be thick and gloppy. That's because it is purging oils and waxes accumulated in a heavy coat. As the warm months wear on, and your horse sweats frequently through a lighter coat, his sweat becomes thinner and clearer.

Normally, horses sweat symmetrically and consistently. Nerve damage in the neck and head, however, can lead to an excess or an absence of sweating in a particular area or side of the body, a condition that needs to be explored by a veterinarian. Dry patches in the sweat marks under tack usually indicate pressure points from an ill-fitting saddle. In very hot, breezy climates, a horse may seem to crust over, rather than sweat. This phenomenon results when sweat evaporates almost instantly, leaving only the mineral crystals on the surface. Excessive sweating is usually caused not by a physical problem but by a heavy coat or mental anxiety. Whatever the reason for sweating, a sopping horse standing in a cool breeze can develop pneumonia. Protect him from chilling with a light sheet or windbreaks as you cool him out.

## The telltale tail

Your horse's tail does much more than swat flies and adorn the rear portion of his anatomy. As an extension of the spinal column, it is one of the most flexible parts of a horse's body. With its muscular ability to move up, down and from side to side, it serves as an excellent means for communication.

The position of a horse's tail usually coincides with the position of his head and neck, and reflects what he may be feeling anywhere along his spine. Consider the following:

- When your horse is relaxed, his tail hangs in a relaxed and natural fashion with no tension.
- If your horse is excited, alert or nervous, he'll hold up his tail and his head and neck, too.
- Holding the tail out, away from the body, is associated with the feeling of being full or constipated.
- Clamping the tail close to the body usually indicates cold, discomfort in your horse's belly or urinary tract, fright or anger (the horse is threatening to kick).
- If your horse is holding his tail up, but his general demeanor is not as energetic, he is probably feeling some discomfort under his tail or is passing gas.

- Tail swishing occurs after urination and defecation, but it can also signal pain or distress. An occasional swish of the tail in response to a rider's seat or leg aid usually indicates that the horse has momentarily tensed his spine out of resistance or discomfort. Constant swishing often points to nervousness or pain (colic, for example).
- If your horse has just had a major workout and his tail is trembling after you dismount, he's probably showing signs of fatigue. An exhausted horse's tail will hang limp and offer no resistance when you pick it up.

## Thumps: equine "hiccups"

The rare and distinctive phenomenon of synchronous diaphragmatic flutter, or "thumps," is the closest thing to hiccups horses get. The nerve impulses that control muscle function are extremely sensitive to calcium, and when tissue levels of this mineral fall due to overexertion or, occasionally, nutritional imbalances, the nerves can "short-circuit."

Thumps occurs when the electrical signals that make the heart beat also excite the phrenic nerve that originates in the brain stem, passes over the heart and ends in the diaphragm muscle, the separation between the chest cavity and the abdomen. With each heartbeat, the diaphragm gives a slight jump, the horse's flanks quiver and a very slight audible gasp—a visible "catch" in his breath—may occur. In extreme cases, the diaphragm muscle contraction causes an audible grunt or thump, hence the condition's name. Once the exhausted horse begins to recover and regain his chemical balance, the rhythmic jump/flutter/gasp ceases.

Although thumps itself poses no direct health risk to the "hiccuping" horse, its occurrence does indicate the need for a management adjustment. Electrolyte supplementation in hot, humid weather often controls the problem by replacing the calcium lost through sweating. A reduction of dietary calcium may also be indicated: Performance horses on high-calcium diets—alfalfa is the usual source—may be more susceptible to thumps during strenuous competition, as their bodies have not practiced mobilizing calcium stores and fail to get the extra mineral into circulation when it's needed.

## Choosing between a tranquilizer and a sedative

Your new filly is very ticklish, making body clipping a real challenge. For everyone's safety, you'd like to give her something to make her more manageable during this necessary grooming event. Do you use a tranquilizer or a sedative? And what's the difference between the two, anyhow?

Although the words are used almost interchangeably by horse owners, "tranquilizer" and "sedative" refer to two different drug types with very distinct actions.

*Tranquilizers,* such as Acepromazine, affect a horse's personality but do nothing to diminish his awareness of physical sensations. They are best used to calm nervousness in a stressed horse, such as a mare who is distraught at weaning time. Because tranquilizers don't impair a horse's physical capabilities, they are useful for quieting horses in situations where balance is important, such as trailering and shoeing. A tranquilized horse subjected to pain or discomfort, however, will most likely act out just as if he hasn't received any drugs. If the horse is not kept quiet for 15 to 20 minutes after administration, the drug may not have the desired tranquilizing effect.

*Sedatives* (Rompun is among the most familiar) make horses less reactive to and less aware of discomfort and pain. They are commonly used in combination with tranquilizers for simple veterinary procedures, such as suturing wounds. Sedatives act more quickly than tranquilizers, and the effects are much more pronounced. A sedated horse may have trouble keeping his balance and need monitoring to be sure he doesn't blunder into trouble. Responses to sedatives are variable from horse to horse, so veterinarians often begin by administering a half-dose to see how the patient responds, then increase the dosage until the desired level of sedation is reached.

Thus, for your ticklish filly who finds clipping a physical torment, a small dose of a sedative—just enough to keep her from acting out—would be the best choice. Watch her carefully until the unbalancing effects wear off.

## What happens when a horse ties up?

Tying up, which is also known as azoturia, occurs when the horse's muscle cells inadequately manage the calcium they contain. Calcium is normally immobilized in special sacs, technically known as cisterns, within each cell. Some of it is released by an electrical impulse, which then causes the muscle to contract. In order for the muscle to relax, the calcium must be returned to the sacs.

If calcium remains outside the sacs, a horse will tie up. There are two ways this can happen. *Type A* tying up occurs at the beginning of exercise. In this instance, the electrical signals come with such intensity and frequency that the muscle cells become flooded with calcium and they cannot relax.

*Type B* occurs at the end of a long, intense workout. In this case, the muscle cells have become so depleted of energy that they cannot pump calcium back into the cisterns. Again, the result is muscle spasm.

Tying up usually affects a horse's large rump muscles and occasionally will

TRAIL READY

*Packing saddlebags with provisions
and spare horseshoes for an hour-long
trail ride may be overkill, but these are
the necessities you really shouldn't be
without, even for quick trips on the trail:*

- *watch*

- *pocketknife*

- *hoof pick*

- *basic first-aid kit for tending horse
and rider*

- *identification on your own person and
attached to your horse*

- *halter and lead rope to tie your horse or
replace broken tack in an emergency.*

involve the thigh or shoulder muscles. In any event, the condition will cause a horse to sweat profusely. If he can walk at all, he will be very stiff and will painfully drag his hind legs.

If you suspect that your horse has tied up, call your veterinarian immediately. Do not try to walk your horse out of the attack as you might to relieve a cramp in your own leg. Although walking horses suffering from Type B tying up may produce a beneficial increase in circulation to the muscles, walking horses with Type A can further stress their already traumatized muscles. Your veterinarian will determine a prompt and proper course of treatment.

Some Quarter Horses and draft crosses tie up because of abnormal polysaccharide storage in their muscles interfering with relaxation. These horses benefit from a low-starch, high-fat diet.

## Three ways to protect horses from ticks

May marks the beginning of the summer tick invasion in many parts of the country. Keeping your horse completely free of ticks is almost impossible, but you can take some steps to protect him from infestation.

**Step 1:** Coat the roots of his mane and tail and his belly and fetlocks with scarlet oil or baby oil once a week. Your horse may become somewhat pink or greasy, but ticks will be unable to attach themselves to those areas.

**Step 2:** During a daily search, use tweezers or a tick-picking device to remove ticks, grasping them close to the skin to be sure the head is removed. A coating of vegetable or mineral oil will cause stubborn suckers to close their air passages and relinquish their hold.

**Step 3:** Drop the removed ticks into a jar of rubbing alcohol, which is the surest and quickest way to kill them. Ticks are very hard to crush, and their juices can spread disease.

## Tack safety check

Before you ride, check your tack for these potential trouble spots:

- elongated or torn holes, cracked or stiff leather, cracked or bent hardware and loose or worn stitching
- on Western saddles, loose or broken D-ring riggings and problems with hobble straps, back cinch billets and connector straps
- on English saddles, stretched or worn billets and stirrup leathers
- on bridles and harnesses, all buckles and any place where leather joins metal.

If you spot a problem, have the part repaired or replaced before using that piece of tack again.

## In perspective: equine recurrent uveitis

Equine recurrent uveitis is an autoimmune disease. Certain agents not normally present in the eye attack the eye, producing chronic, destructive inflammation of the parts of the eyeball served by blood vessels. The condition may flare up intermittently in episodes lasting a few days to a few months. It causes eye redness, tearing, sensitivity to light, haziness or bloodiness of the eye fluid and scarring of the intra-ocular structures. Often, victims experience a single occurrence of the condition and then go into long-term remission, but many endure a succession of flare-ups. Treatment involves administering steroidal and nonsteroidal anti-inflammatories to reduce the swelling that often damages or scars ocular tissues.

## Why horses get ulcers

Ulcers and competitive horses seem to go together. Research indicates that horses' ulcers are far more likely to be caused by physiological than psychological stress. Diet is also a contributor. Studies have shown that pelleted feed and grains spur production of an acid-increasing stomach hormone, while plain hay triggers little release of that same hormone. Living arrangements are a consideration, too.

TERMINOLOGY

ULTRASOUND

*High-frequency sound waves, above the range of human hearing, used to break down unwanted tissue, promote healing by stimulating circulation and aid in accurate diagnosis.*

The best way to prevent ulcers is through careful diet and management changes. Go easy on grain and heavy on hay, and keep your horse turned out as much as possible, especially if he is an elite equine competitor.

## Solutions for umbilical hernias

Umbilical hernias in foals occur when a portion of the intestine or abdominal fat passes through an opening in the abdominal muscle at the "belly button." Umbilical hernias may be present at birth (congenital) or acquired during delivery.

Many umbilical hernias heal on their own as the foal matures. Here's a low-risk home remedy: Cut a clean tennis ball in half and press the furry (rounded) side over the hernia. Palpate and gently coax the hernial pouch back up into the belly, and secure the tennis ball exactly over the spot by wrapping several overlapping turns of adhesive elastic bandage around the foal's torso snugly but not tightly. Check this apparatus daily to be sure the ball stays in place and that the surrounding skin does not become tender or weepy. Replace or adjust the belly band as necessary. Often, the hernia will disappear and seal completely within two to three weeks.

Umbilical hernias also can be treated with the foal sedated and on his back. Your veterinarian will tuck the hernial contents carefully into the abdomen and use a clothespin-like clamp to secure the extra skin. The belly-wall opening closes as the clamped flesh eventually grows together, and the clamp falls off. A drawback to this method is that it may leave a scar.

ALL'S WELL

URINE FACTS

*Horse urine has lots of mucus in it and is normally "ropy" or stringy when it drips. Color varies by both the water content and recent forage, with clovers and alfalfa especially yielding abundant urochromes in the deep-yellow shades.*

## What's behind abnormal urination?

A healthy, resting horse consumes an average of five to seven gallons of water a day, and produces anywhere from one to three gallons of urine. In contrast, a horse with kidney disease may pass a flood of urine no matter how much liquid he consumes. He may drink no more water than usual or he may seem unable to quench his thirst. Whatever the case, his damaged kidneys cannot conserve water and they may purge the body of fluids during times of distress. Instinctively, the horse will usually drink more water to help maintain an adequate level of hydration or to flush out accumulating waste products. His urine may be strong smelling or discolored because of a concentration of waste products, or it may be as pale as light beer.

## Nine vaccines for equine disease

The following equine diseases can be controlled through vaccination:

*Botulism*—food or wound poisoning caused by the toxin secreted by *Clostridium botulinum* bacteria. Botulism is characterized by paralysis, beginning with the muscles of swallowing, and is usually fatal.

*Equine encephalomyelitis* (sleeping sickness)—contagious inflammation of the brain and spinal cord caused by a virus transmitted from birds to horses by mosquitoes. The three primary strains of the disease in horses are eastern equine encephalomyelitis (EEE), western equine encephalomyelitis (WEE) and Venezuelan equine encephalomyelitis (VEE), which is transmissible from horse to horse.

*Equine viral arteritis* (EVA)—a respiratory and venereal disease that can cause abortion.

*Influenza* (two strains: A-Equi-1, A-Equi-2)—extremely contagious viral infection that causes fever, cough, nasal discharge and loss of appetite.

*Potomac horse fever* (monocytic ehrlichiosis)—disease caused by a bacteria-like rickettsial organism, *Ehrlichia risticii*, characterized by fever, diarrhea and laminitis.

*Rabies*—viral disease of the central nervous system, usually fatal.

*Rhinopneumonitis*—contagious disease caused by a virus of the herpes group, characterized by fever and mild respiratory infection. In mares, infection can cause abortion.

*Strangles* (distemper)—highly contagious infection of the lymph nodes of the throat caused by *Streptococcus equi* bacteria. The abscesses may become so large as to obstruct the airway (hence the term "strangles") and may break internally, draining a creamy discharge through the nose.

*Tetanus*—rigid paralytic disease caused by the toxin of *Clostridium tetani,* an anaerobic bacterium that lives in soil and feces, and contaminates wounds.

## Rating ventilation

You don't need fancy equipment to tell if your barn is adequately or overly ventilated. Just use your eyes and nose to rate the quality of the air.

- First, stand in each stall and take a deep breath. Any hint of ammonia means you need to increase ventilation (and improve hygiene) in that stall.
- Walk around the stall a few times to stir up the bedding. Now stop and look across a sunbeam that enters the stall. If you see obvious dust floating in the light shaft, the stall suffers from air stagnation.
- Finally, hold a strip of toilet paper, a few feet in length, out to your side. If it is blown steadily in one direction, the draft in the stall may be strong enough to chill the equine occupant.

*To increase stable ventilation,* replace solid stall doors with stall guards or screens, and/or replace windowpanes with heavy, open-mesh burlap, which will allow air in without causing drafts. Reverse the directional airflow of stall fans so they pull air from the stall instead of blowing it in, making sure fresh air can enter from a nondrafty source.

*To stop chilling drafts,* block openings with solid or semisolid covers, depending on the amount of fresh air needed.

## Very important vitamins

As many as 17 vitamins are involved in various physiologic and metabolic processes, but only a handful have the potential to do harm to horses through excess or deficiency. Six of the most important vitamins in your horse's diet are

**vitamin A** for bone and muscle growth, reproductive function and regeneration of skin tissue. Vitamin A also combines with proteins in the horse's retina to form a substance called rhodopsin ("visual purple"), which is necessary for vision, especially at night.

**vitamin B1** to metabolize carbohydrates and, therefore, extract energy from the diet. B1 also is critical to nervous-system function.

**vitamin D** to help maintain critical electrolyte balance.

**vitamin E,** which combines with the mineral selenium to protect body tissues from free radicals, oxygen molecules that "steal" electrons from other molecules, causing cell destruction.

**vitamin H** to synthesize fats, proteins and glucose. Vitamin H improves hoof and hair quality, although no one knows exactly how.

**vitamin K** for blood clotting and activating a number of proteins so they can be utilized by the body.

## Easing weaning woes

Weaning has long been viewed from the purely practical standpoint of maximizing a dam's productivity. If she's a broodmare, she shouldn't be burdened with a suckling foal any longer than necessary. If she's a working horse, the sooner her foal is weaned, the sooner she'll be able to resume her career.

If you have a solitary mare and foal, the bond between them is likely to be strong. Both will benefit from a gradual weaning strategy that begins with a few minutes spent in separate stalls each day, preferably in the morning. Increase the time by a small amount each day until the foal is nutritionally self-sufficient and the dam is accustomed to the youngster's absence—a process that generally takes about a month. In the later stages of weaning, move the mare out of earshot of the foal, perhaps to a distant field or to a neighbor's farm.

Once the mare is separated permanently from her foal, reduce her calorie intake by providing only hay for several days. Temporarily restrict her water intake to about five gallons per day as well. These measures will help her body slow milk production, thereby avoiding an enlarged udder and possible mastitis—a painful inflammation characterized by hard lumps on the udder. Check the mare's teats regularly for milk buildup, and remove some manually if it becomes excessive. Take care not to milk her out though, because this will stimulate additional milk production.

Some mares may experience separation anxiety to such a degree that they require sedation. Ask your veterinarian if this would help your mare. There also are foals who, for physical or emotional reasons, are too dependent on their dams to be weaned according to a normal schedule. In such cases, it's best to try again in a month or so, when the foal is more self-reliant.

## How much weight can he carry?

Horses in moderate work can comfortably carry as much as 28 percent of their own body weight, including the saddle and the rider. Riders, however, tend to feel most comfortable if they don't weight more than about 20 percent of their horse's weight—meaning that a 200-pound rider using a 15-pound saddle would sit well on a 1,100-pound horse.

## Choose the right wound dressing

Minor cuts and abrasions that afflict horses usually require only the removal of debris and repeated rinsing with saline solution. But even a meticulously cleaned wound sometimes needs extra help. Here are three situations where applying a wound dressing can be beneficial:

- *When contamination is a risk.* Wounds that are exposed to dirt—such as those on the lower legs or on any part of horses who are kept outdoors—can benefit from a thick, waterproof layer of greasy ointment, such as Desitin or ichthammol. Muck and debris will stick to the outside of the ointment, but the wound underneath will be protected.
- *When scabs are slow to form.* Oozy, slow-healing wounds can be encouraged to scab over with powdered antiseptics. Sprayed or puffed onto an area, these powders absorb wound secretions and can help reduce the incidence of proud flesh. Remove loose scabs to treat the healing surface.
- *When flies are feasting.* During warmer months, flies may congregate around wounds and skin irritations, bringing bacteria with them. To ward off pests, apply a thick ointment or a foul-tasting liquid (such as a red-oil preparation) to a wound.

Whatever substance you choose to use to dress a wound, read the label carefully. Mineral oil promotes proud flesh, and alcohol, copper sulfate and strong iodine (seven percent) are caustic and can do additional damage to injured tissue, encouraging the formation of obstructive scabs. Steer clear of wound dressings that contain any of these ingredients.

## The weather-resistant horse

With his weather-resistant design and storm-survival instincts, a naturally kept horse is well prepared to withstand early-spring climate extremes. Thicker skin and a denser hair coat along his back and rump, where rain first strikes, minimize heat loss. The arrangement of the hair channels water to the backs of the legs and a drip spot under the belly. Even during a downpour, thin-skinned vulnerable areas, such as the chest and the inner hind legs, may never get wet.

Not only do horses seek out the least blustery area in their range during a storm, they also adopt a heat-saving stance. Facing away from the wind with lowered heads, horses use their well-padded hindquarters as windbreaks for the rest of their bodies, and their bushy tails as insulation against cold drafts that would chill their underparts.

## What a weight tape tells you about your horse's health

Weight tapes aren't very accurate at telling you how much your horse weighs. While two horses may have the same girth circumference—what you measure with the tape—differences in their body type cause them to weigh different amounts. Yet a weight tape is an excellent measure of *weight change*, a very important indicator of equine health. To monitor weight fluctuations, take and record your horse's measurements with a weight tape once a month as a matter of course, and then weekly or even daily if you suspect an abnormal gain or loss trend.

Consistency in application is key to getting meaningful data from your weighing sessions. Here's how:

**Step 1:** Circle your horse's barrel with the tape in the same place every time you weigh him, just behind the elbows, about where the girth normally goes. In this location, neither his breathing nor a recent large meal will affect the reading.

**Step 2:** Maintain the same moderate tension on the tape, holding it snug against the skin each time you measure. Don't let a thick winter coat add "pounds" to the results.

**Step 3:** Measure at approximately the same time of day and under the same conditions each time. A horse just back from a brisk workout measures thinner than he does after he has cooled out and had a long drink of water.

Every horse participating in strenuous sports has an ideal competition weight, and a variation of as little as 30 or 40 pounds in either direction can take the fine edge off an athletic performance. Seasonal changes or alterations in exercise regimens can cause gradual and acceptable weight fluctuations, but consistent weight loss that doesn't correspond to work or weather or respond to dietary adjustments could indicate that the horse is suffering from systemic illness or parasite infestation. An abrupt drop in weight can occur with serious cases of dehydration or diarrhea.

> ## AT A GLANCE
>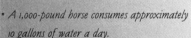
>
> WATER
>
> • *A 1,000-pound horse consumes approximately 10 gallons of water a day.*
>
> • *It takes a horse 48 swallows to drink a gallon of water.*
>
> • *The equine stomach holds three to four gallons of water, which is as much as a very thirsty horse can drink at one time.*
>
> • *A 150-pound person needs just 2 1/2 quarts of water a day.*
>
> • *A camel can drink 33 gallons of water at a time and go up to eight days without drinking.*

**Red Alert:** A sudden weight increase resulting from fluid retention may indicate a life-threatening disorder, such as heart failure or kidney shutdown.

## The wellness checklist

So you'll be better able to recognize the signs that something is amiss, observe your horse when he's feeling fine. Concentrate on these five areas:

**1. Eating**—Pay attention to how fast your horse eats and how long it takes him to finish a meal. Note his feed preferences and what portion of his meal he normally leaves uneaten. Changes in normal eating habits deserve investigation.

**2. Activity**—At what time of day is your horse most active, and when does he choose to rest or doze? How long can you usually ride him before he shows signs of fatigue? Decreased activity or rapid fatigue commonly accompany subtle discomfort or the onset of illness.

**3. Defecation**—Pay attention to the amount, consistency and appearance of your horse's fresh manure. Changes in manure that aren't associated with a ration adjustment can be a sign of parasites, dehydration or other digestive malfunction.

**4. Urination**—There is often noticeable variation in urine from horse to horse and day to day. But take note of very dark or discolored urine that could signal tying up or dehydration. Also, observe your horse's stance and behavior while he urinates. Grunting with urination is normal in some horses, but its sudden onset can indicate discomfort associated with infection or obstruction.

**5. Sleeping**—Some horses lie down several times a day. Others rarely stretch out for a snooze. Observe your horse's normal up-and-down pattern. A horse who suddenly changes sleeping habits may be suffering from hoof pain or a musculoskeletal disorder.

## What are windpuffs?

The generic term "windpuffs" (also known as windgalls) describes soft, painless swellings commonly found near the fetlock joints and occasionally elsewhere on the horse's lower leg. They occur when excessive amounts of synovial fluid fill a stretched fetlock joint capsule or nearby tendon sheath. *Articular windpuffs* develop between the cannon bone and the suspensory ligament. *Tendinous windpuffs* are the residue of tenosynovitis—an inflammation of the digital sheath that surrounds and lubricates the tendons from the ankle to the foot. These swellings are found just behind the suspensory ligament and in front of the digital flexor tendons.

Often appearing together, both types of windpuffs can be caused by
- intense training followed by a period of rest
- excessive exercise on hard surfaces
- the cumulative effects of imbalances produced by poor conformation or improperly trimmed hooves.

New, firm windpuffs on a lame horse may indicate the point of injury. As healing occurs, the stretched tissues may continue to bulge, but they will become soft as soundness returns. Most often, however, windpuffs are simply the mark of years of honest work. Whatever their origin, soft, persistent windpuffs are not harbingers of lameness or performance problems. Bandaging overnight or massaging the area may reduce the swelling temporarily for cosmetic purposes, but established windpuffs almost always return.

## What do X rays show?

X-ray radiographs are particularly useful in depicting alterations in a horse's skeletal structure because of the composition of his bones. Very hard and dense, they are much like stone with fibrous material—blood vessels and nerves—running through them. Most of a bone's weight comes from the calcium, phosphorus, magnesium and trace minerals that give it its structure.

While X rays readily pass through a horse's flesh and are only minimally impeded by his muscle and fatty tissue, they are blocked by his bone. As a result, radiographs of a horse's bony anatomy, especially his limbs, are most beneficial in pinpointing changes in

- *integrity*, such as a fracture
- *position,* such as the dislocation of a joint
- *contour,* such as a deformity
- *density*, such as recurrent trauma with healing—for instance, the process that commonly occurs in the ankles and knees of racehorses.

When are X rays needed? Compare the extent of your horse's condition to the following five guidelines:

1. Radiographs usually provide valuable insight when a horse's injury likely involves bone or a joint and there is evidence of potential disability, for instance, if your horse has had an accident, is three-legged lame and his ankle joint appears swollen.

2. Radiographs can help to characterize chronic disease in or on bone or joints. For example, your horse has been becoming progressively lame in a hind leg and examination reveals that he has extensive low ringbone (arthritis in the coffin joint). Radiographs of the area may show how extensive the bone damage is and give a clue to future expectations.

3. Radiographs are only rarely beneficial in cases of superficial injuries, injuries to the fleshy tissues and injuries in which pain and disability are minimal. For instance, your horse comes in from the pasture limping a bit, but you can find no sign of swelling and within a half hour he is apparently sound, walking and jogging comfortably.

4. Radiographs may be unnecessary if the diagnosis is obvious, for instance, if your veterinarian diagnoses with certainty that your horse's lameness is the result of a severely pulled suspensory ligament.

5. Radiographs of horses who are only slightly lame for two or three days and who have no recent radiographic record are usually useful as a reference tool for later evaluations if the lameness persists.

## What yellow blossoms bode

Ah, spring! Warmer weather, longer days and a riot of golden flowers in your pastures. What could be more beautiful? But two of those cheerful blossoms may be more than a sign of spring. They may signal a need for some pasture-management changes. To protect your horses and preserve your pastures, be prepared to take steps when you see either of these yellow-flowering plants:

Just a few ounces of **buttercups** (*Ranunculus spp.*), low-growing plants with fine leaves and small yellow flowers, are toxic to horses. Fortunately, the bitter taste of buttercups usually discourages their consumption, except by extremely hungry horses. Large quantities of this plant are a sign that your pasture is sparse and poor. Remove horses from a *Ranunculus*-riddled pasture, if possible, or feed hay to rest the pasture until you can reseed.

The common **dandelion** (*Taraxacum officinale*) may be unwelcome in your lawn, but it's a tasty and perfectly harmless pasture plant that your horses will probably eat with gusto. A bumper crop of dandelions, however, is a reminder to give your pasture more time to regenerate, since this plant's wind-borne seeds take root in areas that have been grazed bare the previous year. Try rotating your grazing areas, or reducing the number of animals you keep on any one pasture. Horses like to eat dandelions before the plants go to seed, so as long as your pasture isn't regularly overgrazed, any infestation should be kept in check.

## The source of a yawn

Horses do not apparently yawn from fatigue as people do, at least not after early foalhood. When a horse looks as if he is yawning—he opens his mouth wide and sticks out or lolls his tongue while extending his neck forward and upward—he actually may be reacting to an irritation in the pharynx or back of the mouth.

## Young horses: guidelines for feeding

Assuming that a broodmare has been well fed throughout her pregnancy and that her maternal instincts are intact, her foal can satisfy all of his nutritional needs for the first two months through her milk. After two months, he needs supplemental energy and protein, and after four months, his vitamin and mineral needs are also no longer supplied through nursing. These early months are perhaps the most critical phase in a youngster's nurture—a time of rapid growth, when a declining proportion of his dietary needs comes from his dam's milk.

**VITAL STATISTICS**

YEARLINGS

*A 12-month-old horse's rate of maturation is comparable to that of a 12- or 13-year-old young person. By the time the horse has reached the age of 18 months, he is approaching the equivalent of early adulthood.*

Most foals do just fine with a gradual introduction to grain and hay (access can be aided by creep feeders) and complete the transition to weaning more or less seamlessly. But for many youngsters, getting adequate nutrition is far from easy. Hay can vary in quality from season to season, and in some locales it can be hard to find at all. Too little calcium and phosphorus in the diet can cause skeletal growth problems. On the other hand, when weanlings are fed for maximum growth, as occurs with some sale and show horses, there is a risk that too much dietary energy will cause the bones to grow too quickly or improperly, leading to developmental orthopedic disease.

Several "growth formula" complete feeds offer a simple and safe strategy for feeding youngsters. Feeds for growing horses typically provide higher amounts of protein (15 to 18 percent) and minerals, and lower amounts of fiber (usually less than 15 percent). Some also provide amino acids to boost muscle growth.

## A serving of zinc

Usually supplied in adequate amounts in hay-based diets and commercial feeds, Zinc (Zn) is an important element of protein and carbohydrate metabolism. Horses absorb as much zinc as they need from their diet—anywhere from 5 to 90 percent of their total intake of the mineral. An excess of zinc in the diet interferes with copper utilization. Most cases of toxicosis are related to environmental pollution.

## 5 strategies for protecting horse-friendly zoning

As zoning regulations allow areas to become more densely populated, horse owners across the country are wise to take the necessary steps to cultivate supporters for equestrian interests and influence local zoning decisions. Here are five strategies to help you promote your cause and persuade others that horses can be desirable neighbors.

1. Become active in your community.
2. Keep your horse facility as neat and clean as possible.
3. Keep your nonhorse-owning neighbors happy.
4. Be responsible.
5. Get organized so that you have an established network of horse owners and admirers.

**TERMINOLOGY**

ZOONOSES

*Diseases that can be transmitted from animals to people under natural conditions.*

## Prevent sunburn with zinc oxide

Despite his protective hair coat, the horse is prone to sunburn. Whites, paints and other light-colored horses with a lot of pink skin—the equivalent of fair-skinned people—may either need to be kept indoors during the day or outfitted with a lightweight summer sheet to keep them safe from the sun. Darker horses with white markings may also need extra help. Zinc oxide (that white ointment often worn by lifeguards and beachgoers), aniline dye (such as gentian violet) or even a racing hood can provide protection from the sun.

## Time to catch some z's

While the average person sleeps away a third of his life, the average horse spends only an eighth of his time in dreamland. Awake for an average of 21 hours and 8 minutes a day, the horse is active and alert for 19 hours and 13 minutes and drowsy for 1 hour and 55 minutes. He sleeps during the remaining 2 hours and 52 minutes each day, requiring almost 5 hours less sleep per day than his human counterpart.

# $ SAVE ON FARNAM PRODUCTS $

## $2.00 REBATE ON D-WORM® LIQUID FOR PUPPIES & DOGS
### (any formula)

- Removes large roundworms and hookworms with a wide margin of safety
- Choose D-Worm 60 Liquid or D-Worm 120 Liquid in 2 oz. bottles

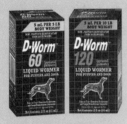

*(see back for complete instructions)*
**Expires 10/31/01**

## $3.00 REBATE ON 2 PACKAGES OF BIO SPOT® FOR DOGS
### (any size)

- Advanced formula spot-on controls immature and adult fleas, plus ticks and mosquitoes
- Available in 3 breed sizes for Small, Medium and Large Dogs

*(see back for complete instructions)*
**Expires 10/31/01**

## $2.00 REBATE ON REPEL-X® P
### (any formula)

- Economical concentrate provides long-lasting fly and pest control
- The horseman's choice for over 40 years

*Available in 16 oz., 32 oz. and gallon sizes*

*(see back for complete instructions)*
**Expires 10/31/01**

## $1.00 REBATE ON ROTECTIN® 2
### (pyrantel pamoate)

- Contains pyrantel pamoate, an excellent compound for rotation with ivermectin

*(see back for complete instructions)*
**Expires 10/31/01**

Fill out this coupon completely and send in along with UPC codes and store receipt (prices circled) to:

**Farnam A to Z Rebate**
P.O. Box 34820, Phoenix, AZ 85067-4820.

**Expires 10/31/01**

Name_____

Address_____

City_____

State _____ Zip_____

Store Where Purchased _____

Allow 4-6 weeks for delivery. Only official certificates accepted. Valid only with original receipt for purchases. Limit one rebate per household or address. All rebates must be postmarked by October 31, 2001. Certificates received after October 31, 2001 or without original receipt for purchases will not be honored. This offer not available to distributors, their salespeople or retailers. Valid in the U.S. only. Void where prohibited. Not valid with any other offer.

| **FOR INTERNAL USE ONLY:** | Vendor #_____ $3.00 | FPP0018 650012.21217 |

 **FARNAM COMPANIES, INC.**

©2000 Farnam Companies, Inc.          0C0

---

Fill out this coupon completely and send in along with UPC codes and store receipt (prices circled) to:

**Farnam A to Z Rebate**
P.O. Box 34820, Phoenix, AZ 85067-4820.

**Expires 10/31/01**

Name_____

Address_____

City_____

State _____ Zip_____

Store Where Purchased _____

Allow 4-6 weeks for delivery. Only official certificates accepted. Valid only with original receipt for purchases. Limit one rebate per household or address. All rebates must be postmarked by October 31, 2001. Certificates received after October 31, 2001 or without original receipt for purchases will not be honored. This offer not available to distributors, their salespeople or retailers. Valid in the U.S. only. Void where prohibited. Not valid with any other offer.

| **FOR INTERNAL USE ONLY:** | Vendor #_____ $2.00 | FPP0017 650012.21230 |

 **FARNAM COMPANIES, INC.**

©2000 Farnam Companies, Inc.          0C0

---

Fill out this coupon completely and send in along with UPC codes and store receipt (prices circled) to:

**Farnam A to Z Rebate**
P.O. Box 34820, Phoenix, AZ 85067-4820.

Name_____

Address_____

City_____

State _____ Zip_____

Store Where Purchased _____

Allow 4-6 weeks for delivery. Only official certificates accepted. Valid only with original receipt for purchases. Limit one rebate per household or address. All rebates must be postmarked by October 31, 2001. Certificates received after October 31, 2001 or without original receipt for purchases will not be honored. This offer not available to distributors, their salespeople or retailers. Valid in the U.S. only. Void where prohibited. Not valid with any other offer.

 **FARNAM COMPANIES, INC.**

©2000 Farnam Companies, Inc.          0C0

---

Fill out this coupon completely and send in along with store receipt (prices circled) to:

**Farnam A to Z Rebate**
P.O. Box 34820, Phoenix, AZ 85067-4820.

Name_____

Address_____

City_____

State _____ Zip_____

Store Where Purchased _____

UPC Code_____

**Expires 10/31/01**

Allow 4-6 weeks for delivery. Only official certificates accepted. Valid only with original receipt for purchases. Limit one rebate per household or address. All rebates must be postmarked by October 31, 2001. Certificates received after October 31, 2001 or without original receipt for purchases will not be honored. This offer not available to distributors, their salespeople or retailers. Valid in the U.S. only. Void where prohibited. Not valid with any other offer.

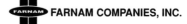 **FARNAM COMPANIES, INC.**

©2000 Farnam Companies, Inc.          0C0

# $ SAVE ON FARNAM PRODUCTS $

## $1.50 REBATE ON LEATHER NEW® LIQUID GLYCERINE SADDLE SOAP
### (any size)

- Cleans, conditions, polishes in one easy step
- Won't dull or stain; leaves no oily residue

*16 oz., 32 oz. and 1/2 gallon sizes*

## $2.00 REBATE ON VETROLIN® PRODUCTS
### (any size, any formula)

- Lavish a little luxury on your horse with Vetrolin
- Choose from liniment, shine or bath formulas

## $5.00 REBATE ON MAXFLEX™ MAXIMUM RELIEF
### (any size, any formula)

- A full range of joint supplements
- Choose from powder or pellets in Glucosamine or Chondroitin formulas

## $2.00 REBATE ON SELECT EQUICARE® FLY CONTROL

- Choose from FlySect® Super 7, Super C Concentrate or Citronella Spray

Fill out this coupon completely and send in along with UPC codes (soak bottle to remove label), store receipt (prices circled) to:

**Farnam A to Z Rebate**
P.O. Box 34820, Phoenix, AZ  85067-4820.

Name_____

Address_____

City_____

State _____ Zip_____

Store Where Purchased _____

### Expires 10/31/01

 **FARNAM COMPANIES, INC.**

©2000 Farnam Companies, Inc.          0C0

---

Fill out this coupon completely and send in along with UPC codes (soak bottle to remove label), store receipt (prices circled) to:

**Farnam A to Z Rebate**
P.O. Box 34820, Phoenix, AZ  85067-4820.

Name_____

Address_____

City_____

State _____ Zip_____

Store Where Purchased _____

### Expires 10/31/01

 **FARNAM COMPANIES, INC.**

©2000 Farnam Companies, Inc.          0C0

---

Fill out this coupon completely and send in along with UPC codes (soak bottle to remove label), store receipt (prices circled) to:

**Farnam A to Z Rebate**
P.O. Box 34820, Phoenix, AZ  85067-4820.

Name_____

Address_____

City_____

State _____ Zip_____

Store Where Purchased _____

### Expires 10/31/01

 **FARNAM COMPANIES, INC.**

©2000 Farnam Companies, Inc.          0C0

---

Fill out this coupon completely and send in along with store receipt (prices circled) to:

**Farnam A to Z Rebate**
P.O. Box 34820, Phoenix, AZ  85067-4820.

Name_____

Address_____

City_____

State _____ Zip_____

Store Where Purchased _____

UPC Code_____

### Expires 10/31/01

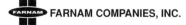 **FARNAM COMPANIES, INC.**

©2000 Farnam Companies, Inc.          0C0

# $ SAVE ON FARNAM PRODUCTS $

## $2.00 REBATE ON TRI-TEC 14™
### (any size)

- Combines botanically-derived pyrethrins with cypermethrin for long-lasting control

- Repels and kills flies and other insects up to 14 days

*Available in 32 oz. with trigger sprayer or gallon*

## $2.00 REBATE ON HORSESHOER'S SECRET™
### (any size)

- Helps prevent cracked hoofs and weak walls, restore normal hoof growth, and helps hoofs hold shoes longer

*Available in 11 lb., 22 lb. and 38 lb. buckets*

## $2.00 REBATE ON WEIGHT BUILDER™
### (any size)

- Provides extra calories for equine weight gain, body condition and fuel for performance

*Available in 8 lb. and 28 lb. buckets*

## $2.00 REBATE ON FLUIDFLEX™
### (quart size only)

- The most complete, natural supplement available for relieving the symptoms of equine joint degeneration

- You could see results in your horse in as little as 5 days

Fill out this coupon completely and send in along with store receipt (prices circled) to:

**Farnam A to Z Rebate**
P.O. Box 34820, Phoenix, AZ 85067-4820.

Name_____

Address_____

City _____

State _____ Zip_____

Store Where Purchased _____

UPC Code_____

### Expires 10/31/01

Allow 4-6 weeks for delivery. Only official certificates accepted. Valid only with original receipt for purchases. Limit one rebate per household or address. All rebates must be postmarked by October 31, 2001. Certificates received after October 31, 2001 or without original receipt for purchases will not be honored. This offer not available to distributors, their salespeople or retailers. Valid in the U.S. only. Void where prohibited. Not valid with any other offer.

 **FARNAM COMPANIES, INC.**

©2000 Farnam Companies, Inc.          0C0

---

Fill out this coupon completely and send in along with UPC codes (soak bottle to remove label), store receipt (prices circled) to:

**Farnam A to Z Rebate**
P.O. Box 34820, Phoenix, AZ 85067-4820.

Name_____

Address_____

City _____

State _____ Zip_____

Store Where Purchased _____

### Expires 10/31/01

Allow 4-6 weeks for delivery. Only official certificates accepted. Valid only with original receipt for purchases. Limit one rebate per household or address. All rebates must be postmarked by October 31, 2001. Certificates received after October 31, 2001 or without original receipt for purchases will not be honored. This offer not available to distributors, their salespeople or retailers. Valid in the U.S. only. Void where prohibited. Not valid with any other offer.

 **FARNAM COMPANIES, INC.**

©2000 Farnam Companies, Inc.          0C0

---

Fill out this coupon completely and send in along with UPC codes (soak bottle to remove label), store receipt (prices circled) to:

**Farnam A to Z Rebate**
P.O. Box 34820, Phoenix, AZ 85067-4820.

Name_____

Address_____

City _____

State _____ Zip_____

Store Where Purchased _____

### Expires 10/31/01

Allow 4-6 weeks for delivery. Only official certificates accepted. Valid only with original receipt for purchases. Limit one rebate per household or address. All rebates must be postmarked by October 31, 2001. Certificates received after October 31, 2001 or without original receipt for purchases will not be honored. This offer not available to distributors, their salespeople or retailers. Valid in the U.S. only. Void where prohibited. Not valid with any other offer.

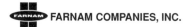 **FARNAM COMPANIES, INC.**

©2000 Farnam Companies, Inc.          0C0

---

Fill out this coupon completely and send in along with store receipt (prices circled) to:

**Farnam A to Z Rebate**
P.O. Box 34820, Phoenix, AZ 85067-4820.

Name_____

Address_____

City _____

State _____ Zip_____

Store Where Purchased _____

UPC Code_____

### Expires 10/31/01

Allow 4-6 weeks for delivery. Only official certificates accepted. Valid only with original receipt for purchases. Limit one rebate per household or address. All rebates must be postmarked by October 31, 2001. Certificates received after October 31, 2001 or without original receipt for purchases will not be honored. This offer not available to distributors, their salespeople or retailers. Valid in the U.S. only. Void where prohibited. Not valid with any other offer.

 **FARNAM COMPANIES, INC.**

©2000 Farnam Companies, Inc.          0C0

# The leading source of horse-care information.

For more than 20 years, *EQUUS* has been an invaluable tool for people dedicated to providing their horses with the best care possible. Its award-winning articles on veterinary advances, hands-on horse care, equine behavior, riding and training will help you to make the most of your time with your horse.

Simply return the attached card to take advantage of this exclusive limited offer.

Photo by Martha Bell

# EQUUS

# EQUUS

*Your horse-care encyclopedia*

- Stay up to date on the latest veterinary advances – the best new treatments, innovative surgical procedures and promising developments in drug therapy.

- Learn about the inner working of the horse's body and mind.

- Hear what the experts have to say about everything from vaccination schedules to rehabilitating a barn-sour horse.

- Build your own reference library of *EQUUS* issues so you'll always have easy access to information you need to ensure your horse's health and happiness.